The Spencer Collection
of American Art

An Exhibition of Works for Sale

June 13–29, 1990

Spanierman Gallery

50 East 78th Street   New York, NY 10021   Telephone (212) 879-7085   Fax (212) 249-5227

Gallery hours: Tuesday through Saturday, 9:30 a.m. to 5:30 p.m.

WE HAVE truly enjoyed producing this catalogue. Our first thanks are due, of course, to Ralph and Florence Spencer, who have been gracious, thoughtful, and generous through all phases of this effort. It has been a delight to work with them and to catalogue and study the splendid works in their collection. We would also like to express appreciation to our contributing authors, who provided illuminating and informative essays. In addition, many Spanierman Gallery staff members helped to organize the exhibition and compile the catalogue. Carol Lowrey did an excellent job as bibliographic editor. Jean Carlson provided essential assistance with research and editing. Others who participated include Lisa Bogan, Laurene Buckley, Gregg Deering, Douglas Denton, Suzanne Denton, Stephen Edidin, Anna Erdelyi, Michael Horvath, Betty Krulik, Ellery Kurtz, Suzanne Meadow, Mary Nowak, Kevin Phillips, Christine Rossi, Judy Salerno, Gavin Spanierman, and Estelle Yanco. We would also like to thank David Sassian for editing this catalogue with care.

Lisa N. Peters
David C. Henry

Cover:
Theodore Robinson (1852–1896)
White Bridge on the Canal, 1893
Oil on canvas
15 × 22 inches

Introduction

IN THE mid-1960s no one knew who the Ten were. Roy Davis and I saw references to the organization here and there, but the painters were never listed. As a matter of fact, in those days if you could name the Eight you were considered quite an expert in American art. We were aware, however, that Hassam and Chase were members of a mysterious group called the Ten. One day, after Roy and I had puzzled for a long time over the Ten, he called me excitedly and I ran over to his gallery on East 60th Street. He had found a book with a photograph of the Ten American Painters. In the caption underneath, all the members were listed. It was a very exciting moment. Now that we're doing a show on the Ten, we are amazed to discover just how much was written about the group during its era. The artists and the organization have, of course, become quite recognized over the last twenty-five years.

I met Ralph and Florence Spencer at the time that I was becoming aware of the Ten, at a time when American art collecting was just beginning to blossom. They came into the gallery about twenty-seven or twenty-eight years ago when we were on Lexington Avenue. In those days, people went out to the galleries every Saturday to look around and to shop, and they could buy good paintings that weren't terribly expensive. There was a cache of fine things available. Ralph and Florence made weekly Saturday excursions. They chose wisely and with great perception and taste, gathering a collection of remarkable quality. Among their choices were significant works by six members of the Ten—Frank W. Benson, William Merritt Chase, Thomas Dewing, Childe Hassam, John Twachtman, and J. Alden Weir—as well as paintings by American masters George Bellows, Robert Henri, John La Farge, Maurice Prendergast, Theodore Robinson, and John Singer Sargent. The high caliber, excellence, and beauty of the works they assembled is notable, and their collection compares favorably with those of the finest museums. The quality is just not available anymore. We are very glad to be able to catalogue for exhibition and sale the beautiful and important late nineteenth- and early twentieth-century works that Ralph and Florence Spencer gathered with such great devotion and pleasure.

Ira Spanierman

Thomas Pollock Anshutz (1851–1912)

1. *Near Cape May*, 1894

Two-sided watercolor on paper
9½ × 13½ inches
Signed and dated by Edward R. Anshutz, the artist's
son on verso: *by Thos. P. Anshutz / 1894 A.N.A.*

Provenance:
Estate of Thomas Anshutz
to (James Graham & Sons, New York), 1966
to Mr. and Mrs. Ralph Spencer, 1966

UNTIL THE early 1960s, the Philadelphia painter Thomas Pollock Anshutz was known primarily as a student and follower of Thomas Eakins and was seen as having little artistic identity of his own. At that point, however, with the examination of newly discovered watercolors, Anshutz began to gain recognition as a talented, original artist in his own right. Although his works in oil—especially his carefully studied portraits and genre scenes—clearly reflect a debt to his teacher, his watercolors show his inventive and spontaneous side. Hidden for years in the artist's estate, the watercolors reveal a fascinating aspect of the artist that had been virtually unknown to the public.

Anshutz worked for many years under the shadow of Eakins. He had assisted Eakins in teaching at the Pennsylvania Academy of the Fine Arts, then took on greater responsibilities when the older man was forced to resign in 1886. Up to this point, and for a few years afterward, Anshutz had painted in a traditional style, mostly in oil. But in September 1892 he began a year's sojourn in Paris, where he absorbed the art of the Impressionists and the Nabis. In France he produced a number of fresh, brightly colored landscapes in watercolor. And when he returned to Philadelphia, he continued to work in this medium, notably during painting trips to the New Jersey shore, particularly Cape May, a fashionable resort.

Near Cape May, portraying a woman seated in a dory, is typical of the watercolors Anshutz executed on his summer outings. In this work the artist has employed a palette rich in blues, greens, ochers, and purples. His colors are applied broadly, with bold, confident strokes; because he did not rework his hues, the sheet remains bright and luminous, echoing the spirit of Winslow Homer's watercolors. Like that earlier master of the medium, Anshutz understood the value of simplicity, immediacy, and freshness of effect. Related works, equally drenched in sunlight, show young boys or women on the beach, often in or near a sailboat or a dory similar to that of *Near Cape May*. And while the compositions may contain a larger number of figures than the present example, all of the works display a characteristic mastery of light and broadness of treatment.

From time to time Anshutz painted on both sides of the paper. No doubt he followed this practice, not uncommon among watercolor painters, because he wanted to improve upon his initial effort. Convenience or economy, or both, dictated that he use the remaining side for another picture. In the case of *Near Cape May*, what may have been his first trial—an unpopulated inlet with several dories and a small sailboat—appears on the reverse side of the sheet. This attempt, pale in color, is tentative compared to the fully developed view of the woman in a dory that is the principal subject of the work on the other side. *Near Cape May* is a peaceful work, vibrant in color, with a monumentality belying the intimate scale of the painting.

William Innes Homer

Milton Avery (1893–1965)

2. *Pine Grove*, 1955

Oil crayon and gouache on paper
24 × 18 inches
Signed and dated lower left: *Milton Avery '55*
Inscribed verso: *Pine Grove*

Provenance:
Estate of Milton Avery
to Mr. and Mrs. Ralph Spencer, ca. 1983

MILTON AVERY, admired for his lyrical, Matisse-inspired colorism and his poetic approach toward nature, is regarded as one of America's most important artists of the twentieth century. A vital force in the development of modernism in the United States, Avery's work exerted a major influence on the Abstract Expressionist and color-field painters of the 1950s and 1960s. Although his subject matter was always recognizable, he achieved a subtle balance between representation and abstraction, endowing his oeuvre with a mysterious, inner sensibility.

Like many artists who lived and worked in New York, Avery spent his summers away from the city, finding relief from the heat and lassitude of Manhattan, as well as artistic inspiration, in such picturesque regions as Gloucester, Massachusetts, and the Gaspé Peninsula, in Quebec, Canada. Accompanied by his family, he made numerous trips to these and other sites in the Northeast from the 1920s until 1949, when he suffered a heart attack.

The Averys continued to take summer vacations during the 1950s, although, with the exception of a trip to Europe in 1952, they now tended to seek out peaceful, more reclusive locales. In addition to visiting Woodstock, New York, and Provincetown, Massachusetts, they were summer residents at two of America's most experimental art colonies. In 1953, 1954 and 1956, Avery and his wife, Sally, held fellowships at the MacDowell Colony in Peterborough, New Hampshire, while the summer of 1955 was spent at Yaddo, a quiet retreat for artists, musicians, and writers situated on the outskirts of Saratoga Springs, New York.

Founded in 1926, the Yaddo colony (which is still active today) comprises almost five hundred acres of formal parks, pine forests, lakes, a rose garden, and a large Gothic mansion built at the turn of the century by the noted philanthropist Spencer Trask and his wife, the poet Katrina Nichols.[1] Unlike other art colonies, especially those based on late nineteenth-century French prototypes, both Yaddo and the MacDowell Colony stressed the concept of creative isolation. Thus, between the hours of 9:00 a.m. and 4:30 p.m., Avery would have confined himself to his studio, located in a secluded spot somewhere on the estate, to paint and sketch on his own. Not until the evenings, when he returned to the main house, would he have resumed any communal activity, fraternizing with his family and other guests, such as the poet Horace Gregory or the composer Richard Donovan. It was in this utopian setting that Avery produced a number of oils, drawings, and watercolors, including *Pine Grove*, an intimate rendering of the lush scenery he would have encountered on the Yaddo estate.

Avery's composition, possibly a study for a larger painting, is dominated by a group of tall pine trees that loom over an ambiguous wooden structure, seemingly a shed or covered bridge. Employing a reduced palette dominated by fresh greens and blues and accented by touches of black and warmer earth tones, he juxtaposes soft, broad modulations of the crayon, evident, for example, in the sky, with a fluid, more vigorous application of gouache for the foliage. This approach, as well as his method of allowing portions of the underlying paper to emerge and mingle with the crayon, gives the scene a lively surface animation and vibrancy as well as a sense of atmosphere. These effects, quite different from the two-dimensional qualities evident in his oils, are enhanced by the application of the transparent gouache, which surrounds, but does not permeate, the crayon.

Although Avery has used the point of his crayon to produce a number of linear accents, such as those on the roof of the cabin and on various branches of the trees, detail has generally been eliminated, the artist preferring instead to focus on capturing the "essence" of his subject matter. The gentle lyricism that pervades this work is typical of Avery's aesthetic, inspired, above all else, by his very private vision of nature.

Carol Lowrey

1. See "Yaddo and Substance," *Time* 32 (5 September 1938): 50; Jacob Getlar Smith, "Yaddo: A Working Community for Artists," *American Artist* 19 (March 1955): 54–55; and Bradford Smith, "Parnassus, USA: Three Sanctuaries for the Artist," *Saturday Review* 42 (2 August 1958): 7–10; 40–41. Other well-known guests at Yaddo included Katherine Anne Porter, Saul Bellow, William Carlos Williams, and Leonard Bernstein. The name "Yaddo" was the Trask children's way of pronouncing "The Shadows," an old tavern formerly on the site of the family property.

George Bellows (1882–1925)

3. *Wave*, 1913[1]

Oil on panel
15 × 19½ inches
Signed lower left: *Geo. Bellows*

Provenance:
Estate of the artist, 1925
to Emma S. Bellows, the artist's wife, 1925
to Estate of Emma S. Bellows, 1959
to (H. V. Allison & Co., New York), 1959–1966
to Mr. and Mrs. Ralph Spencer, 1966

This work will be included in the forthcoming catalogue raisonné of the paintings of George Bellows by Glenn C. Peck.

GEORGE BELLOWS'S action-packed oil titled *Wave* was painted on Monhegan Island, Maine, during the summer of 1913. Bellows had initially visited this tiny, isolated speck in the Atlantic two years before in the company of his revered former teacher, Robert Henri. Bellows had seen Henri's invitation to join him there as an opportunity to escape the heat of Montclair, New Jersey, and the trauma of staying with in-laws while his wife sat out the final months of her pregnancy.

During a six-week period on Monhegan in August and September 1911, Bellows painted a dozen canvases and thirty pochades (small oil paintings on wood panels) before returning just in time to witness the birth of his daughter and, belatedly, to celebrate his own twenty-ninth birthday.

Intrigued by the variety of subject matter available on Monhegan—the island, only one by two miles, contains a harbor full of dories, barren land at sea level, a dense forest area, and two hundred foot high cliffs—Bellows was eager to visit there again the following summer. However, his wife Emma dreaded the thought of a two-hour voyage by sailboat seventeen miles out into the Atlantic, and she argued successfully that their infant was too young for such travel. Emma got her way in 1912, but the next summer it was George's turn, and off to Monhegan they went, alone this time because Henri was painting in Ireland.

Even without his former instructor, whom Bellows referred to as "my father in Art," he continued to live and paint by Henri's philosophy, using a spontaneous approach, wielding a brush with verve and dash.[2] Among the pochades Bellows produced that summer, *Wave*, which features a sculpturesque build-up of pigment, is surely clear testimony to his technical prowess.

Henri's earlier pochades of the caldronlike sea around Monhegan Island had captured the swirling water as it pounded the rocks, producing spray and foam before flowing back with the tide. Bellows's similar efforts, epitomized by *Wave*, go one step further in their expressionistic vigor—the thrust of an angry ocean, which diminishes in intensity of both brushwork and color as it dissolves along a distant gray horizon.

Here the long, diagonal shadow of the foreground wave serves as a foil to the other deep, dark diagonal, a cliff that plunges down from the left-hand corner of the composition. And the billowing areas of white spray—one of which repeats the silhouette of the rock on the left, while both interrupt the picture's lone horizontal, the subtle horizon line—are sufficient to prevent the visual isolation of the picture's upper reaches. Few artists have been able to capture the excitement of a wave and the allure of an angry Atlantic as well as George Bellows does here.

Bennard B. Perlman

1. *Wave* is recorded in the artist's Private Record Book A, p. 221, Estate of Emma S. Bellows.
2. Mrs. George (Emma) Bellows, interview with author, 25 January 1957.

George Bellows

4. *Horses, Carmel*, 1917[1]

Oil on panel
17¾ × 22 inches
Signed lower left: *Geo. Bellows*

Provenance:
Estate of the artist, 1925
to Emma S. Bellows, the artist's wife, 1925
to Estate of Emma S. Bellows, 1959
to (H. V. Allison and Co., New York), 1959–1965
to Mr. and Mrs. Ralph Spencer, 1965

Exhibited:
Oakland Art Gallery, *George Bellows Exhibition of
    Lithographs and Paintings*, 15–30 September 1917.

This work will be included in the forthcoming
    catalogue raisonné of the paintings of George
    Bellows by Glenn C. Peck.

THE PROMISE of a portrait commission lured George Bellows to Carmel, California, in May 1917. Joined by his wife and two young daughters, he set up headquarters in "the 'Queen's Castle,'" as he referred to it in a letter to Robert Henri, "the most pretentious dwelling here with lots of rooms and a fine garden of flowers and trees looking on the sea and almost on the beach."[2]

There were many subjects to attract him, and some centered on the beach itself, with its fine white sand contrasting with lush, imposing headlands. It was here that Bellows painted *The Sand Team*, 1917 (The Brooklyn Museum, New York), depicting several men shoveling sand into a wagon hitched to four white horses, as well as *Horses, Carmel*, 1917. Both works are nearly unique subjects in Bellows's oeuvre, which is so dominated by cityscapes, boxing matches, and single portraits and figures.

The Sand Team and *Horses, Carmel* present an interesting compositional contrast, for while they each show an expanse of land in the foreground and rolling hills beyond, separated by a finger of intense blue water, the horses in the former occupy much of the lower half of the picture, while those in *Horses, Carmel* are arranged friezelike, just above the bottom of the frame.

The horses in this painting are masterfully placed. Not only are they arranged to provide a variety of spatial relationships among themselves and between the group and the darkened pasture of the middleground, but the varied poses and colors elevate the lower quarter of the painting to a self-contained composition within the whole. Bellows has balanced the two gray horses on the left with a pair of white ones on the right, then painted the body of the center one with purple reflections, fully aware that this cool hue is the complementary color of the warm yellow surrounding it.

Further defying the natural appearance of things, the artist chooses to emphasize the texture of the terrain in the middle- and background; thus a nearby field is covered with thin pigment while more distant vegetation is represented by paint applied with a heavily loaded brush.

Bellows's visit to California was all too brief, for once the portrait commission was completed, he decided to join Henri in Santa Fe, and it was there that the two artists and their families spent the remainder of the summer. *Horses, Carmel* is one of the wondrous reminders of Bellows's 1917 sojourn to the West Coast.

Bennard B. Perlman

1. *Horses, Carmel* is recorded in the artist's Private Record Book B (as *Horses*), p. 114, Estate of Emma S. Bellows.
2. Charles H. Morgan, *George Bellows: Painter of America* (New York: Reynal & Co., 1965), p. 218.

Frank W. Benson (1862–1951)

5. *Woman with Geraniums*, ca. 1910

Oil on canvas
28 × 22 inches
Signed lower right: *F. W. Benson*

Provenance:
(Mr. William Koch, Mobile, Alabama)
(Spanierman Gallery, New York) ca. 1969–1970
to Mr. and Mrs. Ralph Spencer ca. 1969–1970

Exhibited:
Whitney Museum of American Art, New York,
    *Eighteenth and Nineteenth Century American Art
    from Private Collections*, 1972, no. 1.
Spanierman Gallery, New York, *Frank W. Benson: The
    Impressionist Years*, 11 May–11 June 1988, no. 62
    (p. 63 col. ill.).

Literature:
Sheila Dugan, "Frank Benson: Outdoors," in John
    Wilmerding, Sheila Dugan, and William H.
    Gerdts, *Frank W. Benson: The Impressionist Years*,
    exh. cat. (New York: Spanierman Gallery, 1988),
    p. 21.

FROM 1900 until about 1920, during summers spent on North Haven Island, Maine, Frank Benson created works that depart from the somber interiors reminiscent of Jan Vermeer that he rendered during the winter months in his Salem, Massachusetts studio. Liberated by the invigorating air and the expansive coastal terrain, he adopted a vibrant, dynamic, Impressionist style and began to render figures *en plein air*.[1] The artist's daughters and their friends, dressed in white, are shown standing on hilltops, silhouetted against the sky, or seated on sloping landscapes, the countryside stretching out beyond them. Absorbed in thought or gazing across broad vistas, they appear transfixed by the beauty of the scenery.

In *Woman with Geraniums*, Benson depicts a figure on a hillside lost in reverie, her reflections undoubtedly encouraged by the peaceful beauty of her surroundings. As in other North Haven works, such as *Sunlight* (Indianapolis Museum of Art), *Elisabeth and Anna—In Summer* (private collection) and *Eleanor* (Museum of Fine Arts, Boston), Benson portrays a woman in profile and positions her broadly within the canvas. The profile view allowed Benson to render his sitters in general terms and to create strong designs in which figure and landscape are given equal prominence. In *Woman with Geraniums*, the canvas is divided in half on a diagonal axis. The result is a simple and unified arrangement that recalls Benson's decorative murals of the mid-1890s.[2]

In North Haven, Benson experimented with capturing different light effects. He painted many scenes at midday, for example *The Hilltop* (Malden [Mass.] Public Library), in which light falls directly on the figure who stands full-length in the composition. However, in other works, such as *Afternoon in September* (Natural History Museum of Los Angeles County) and *Children in the Woods* (Metropolitan Museum of Art, New York), Benson presents transitional times of the day, capturing dappled light effects and subtle shifts of tone. *Woman with Geraniums* was probably rendered in the late afternoon, as sun streaks across the figure, illuminating the front of her white, high-collared dress, while much of the rest of the scene is more softly lit. Warm shadows in the meadow complement the woman's introspective attitude.

Many artists of the late nineteenth century created paintings of women outdoors in gardens or amidst fields of flowers.[3] Indeed, this was a favored subject of a number of Benson's colleagues in the Ten American Painters, particularly Robert Reid, John Twachtman, Childe Hassam, and William Merritt Chase, who often associated the beauty of their sitters with that of their floral settings. Here Benson also unites figures with flowers. As Sheila Dugan wrote of *Woman with Geraniums*: "Benson's main intention is one of blending the components of the woman with the surrounding floral environment, in essence establishing her as the main flower among all the others."[4]

Benson's treatment of flowers demonstrates the fluidity and confidence of his Impressionist style. He paints red geraniums with loose and painterly swirls of pigment that express their animated shapes. Rendered directly and spontaneously, their stalks and leaves are also lively and vivid. In contrast, the meadow is more softly painted, with patches of yellow and green suggesting shifting patterns of light falling gently across the scene.

In *Woman with Geraniums*, Benson reinterprets the Boston School aesthetic in outdoor terms, depicting a contemplative subject engaged in a daydream. The meditative mood of the woman is perfectly matched by the tranquil landscape that surrounds her. The painting captures the leisurely pleasure and the solace offered by an idyllic summer afternoon on the Maine coast.

Lisa N. Peters

1. For an overview of Benson's North Haven works, see John Wilmerding, Sheila Dugan, and William H. Gerdts, *Frank W. Benson: The Impressionist Years*, exh. cat. (New York: Spanierman Gallery, 1988).
2. In the mid-1890s, Benson created two series of mural paintings for the new Library of Congress building in Washington, D.C., one depicting the Three Graces and the other the Four Seasons.
3. For a comprehensive discussion of American artists's depictions of garden imagery, see William H. Gerdts, *Down Garden Paths: The Floral Environment in American Art*, exh. cat. (Rutherford, N. J.: Fairleigh Dickinson University Press [for the Montclair Art Museum, Montclair, N. J.]), 1983.
4. Sheila Dugan, "Frank Benson: Outdoors," in John Wilmerding, Sheila Dugan, and William H. Gerdts, *Frank W. Benson: The Impressionist Years*, p. 22.

Dennis Miller Bunker (1861–1890)

6. *Brittany Town Morning, Larmor*, 1884

Oil on canvas
14 × 22 inches
Signed and dated lower left: *Dennis M. Bunker/
Larmor/1884*

Provenance:
(Sotheby Parke Bernet, New York, 28 April 1977,
 no. 153)
to (Spanierman Gallery, New York), 1978
to Mr. and Mrs. Ralph Spencer, 1978

Exhibited:
Noyes & Blakeslee Gallery, Boston, *Dennis Miller
 Bunker Exhibition*, 1885, no. 10.
National Academy of Design, New York, *Sixtieth
 Annual Exhibition*, 6 April–16 May 1885, no. 192.
New Britain Museum of American Art, New Britain,
 Conn., *Dennis Miller Bunker (1861–1890)
 Rediscovered*, 1 April–7 May 1978, no. 10 (pl. 10
 col. ill.).
Norton Gallery of Art, West Palm Beach, Fla., *In
 Nature's Ways: American Landscape Painting of the
 Late Nineteenth Century*, 21 February–12 April
 1987, no. 6 (p. 46 col. ill.). Circulating exhibition,
 1987.

Literature (partial list):
Charles B. Ferguson, *Dennis Miller Bunker (1861–
 1890) Rediscovered*, exh. cat. (New Britain, Conn.:
 New Britain Museum of American Art, 1978),
 [pp. 7–8], pl. 10 col. ill.
Jolene Goldenthal, "Forgotten Impressionist," *Hartford
 Courant*, 2 April 1978, p. 2G ill.
William H. Gerdts, *American Impressionism* (New
 York: Abbeville Press, 1984), pp. 84, 85 ill.
Efrat Adler Porat, "Dennis Miller Bunker (1861–1890):
 Pioneer for American Impressionist Landscape,"
 Master's thesis, Tufts University, 1984, pp. 93,
 210 ill.
Bruce Weber, "In Nature's Ways: American Landscape
 Painting of the Late Nineteenth Century," in
 Bruce Weber and William H. Gerdts, *In Nature's
 Ways: American Landscape Painting of the Late
 Nineteenth Century*, exh. cat. (West Palm Beach,
 Fla.: Norton Gallery of Art, 1987),
 pp. 12–13, p. 46 col. ill.

IN DENNIS MILLER BUNKER's short life he painted some brilliant pictures. One of these is *Brittany Town Morning, Larmor*.

Bunker was born in New York City and attended the New York Art Students League and the National Academy of Design. He also received instruction from William Merritt Chase. In 1882, at age twenty-one, Bunker went to Paris to further his education, studying at the Académie Julian and at the Ecole des Beaux-Arts with Jean-Léon Gérôme. He returned to the United States in 1885.

Bunker's painting excursion in the summer of 1884 to Larmor, a small town on the southwest coast of Brittany, produced several of his finest canvases to date.[1] By this time Bunker had a firm grounding in figure drawing and portrait rendering. However, he also had a passion for landscape. Before 1884 he had painted in and around New York, Long Island, and Nantucket, Massachusetts. During these ventures, he had painted directly from his subjects, and in the summer of 1884 he made even greater strides in the depiction of sunlight and atmosphere. Inspired by the art of the Barbizon painter Camille Corot, Bunker began to work *en plein air*, an approach that led not only to *Brittany Town Morning*, but also to the magnificent Impressionist landscapes he created during the last two years of his life.

Brittany Town Morning is, in the opinion of this writer, one of the great landscapes executed by an American artist while in Europe. With its compositional structure emphasized by strengthening architectural elements, the painting resembles the landscapes Corot rendered in Italy. There are three other Larmor paintings, also architectural landscapes, but *Brittany Town Morning*, with its massive church tower and silhouetted townscape, is the most monumental.[2] Bunker chose to paint the town in the early morning, placing his easel toward the sun, depicting gleaming roofs that contrast with the shadowed sides of buildings and the dominating church spire. There is an elegant balance of verticals and horizontals in the work that creates stability and conveys serenity.

Bunker counters the strongly massed forms of the middleground with a soft and colorful treatment of the foreground. Dappled light effects are evident in the broad, glistening landscape, imbuing the work with life. The dominant green is mixed with a range of colors from yellow, to orange, to reddish browns.

The small figure of the Breton woman laying out her wash to dry is a masterly touch. The figure not only gives a sense of scale and depth to the painting, but also enables Bunker to introduce small splashes of two primary colors, red and blue. One can imagine a little brook where the washing was done, meandering through the grass and small bushes.

Wonderfully composed and orchestrated, *Brittany Town Morning* is the keystone work of Bunker's Larmor series. The painting reflects Bunker's stylistic progression, from the plein-air approach of his French years to the very personal Impressionism that blossomed in the floral paintings of 1888 and the landscapes he painted in the fields and along the little brook in Medfield, Massachusetts, from 1888 to 1890.[3] Bunker's career was very short; he died tragically at age twenty-nine of influenza. Had he been able to further his exploration of Impressionism, there is no doubt that he would be better recognized today and would take his rightful place alongside Childe Hassam, Willard Metcalf, Theodore Robinson, and John Twachtman.

Charles B. Ferguson

1. No other artists are known to have painted in Larmor. The town was not associated with artists as were others in Brittany, such as Pont-Aven or Concarneau.
2. For information on and reproductions of Bunker's Larmor paintings, see R. H. Ives Gammell, *Dennis Miller Bunker* (New York: Coward-McCann, 1953), second plate following p. 50; Charles B. Ferguson, *Dennis Miller Bunker*, nos. 10–12; Efrat Adler Porat, "Dennis Miller Bunker," p. 91, fig. 20.
3. Bunker met John Singer Sargent through Isabella Stewart Gardner in January 1888 in Boston where Sargent's works were being exhibited. That summer Bunker traveled to Calcot, England, where he painted alongside Sargent. By then Sargent knew of Claude Monet's theories and techniques, and while he had adopted some of them, he had forged his own distinctive flashy style. During this summer Monet's Impressionist approach, as filtered through Sargent, passed to Bunker.

William Merritt Chase (1849–1916)

7. *Portrait of a Lady*, 1893[1]

Oil on canvas
21 × 17 inches
Signed and dated lower right: *Wm. M. Chase/1893*

Provenance:
(Kennedy Galleries, New York)
(Paul Magriel, New York)
(Hirschl & Adler Galleries, New York), 1964
to Mr. and Mrs. Ralph Spencer, 1965

This work will be included in the forthcoming catalogue raisonné of the work of William Merritt Chase by Ronald G. Pisano.

WILLIAM MERRITT CHASE believed that artists derived more pleasure from portrait painting than from any other genre. The unique character of each sitter provided the portrait painter with constant variety and challenge. In Chase's estimation there were four components to a successful portrait: simplicity, dignity, style, and technique.[2] While realizing the importance of capturing the personality of each sitter, Chase stressed that each portrait should first and foremost be a work of art rather than a mere likeness. "I never slavishly work for a likeness," Chase proclaimed, "and yet I paint realistically the effects of colour, of form, and of light; and in the painting the character of the sitter comes without conscious striving for it."[3] The magic by which Chase turned likeness and personality into art can be observed in his spontaneously painted portraits. The enduring appeal of these works can be attributed in part to this magic, but it is also due to the obvious delight Chase experienced in painting them with self-confidence and ease. An impressive range of portrait types—some commissioned, some intended for exhibition, and others painted for his private pleasure—are lasting evidence of Chase's versatility as a portrait painter.

Portrait of a Lady, 1893 clearly displays the attributes Chase designated as essential for the successful portrait. It is simple in conception, dignified in its expression of character, and stylishly painted. Its masterful technique is apparent in the rich and swiftly applied paint strokes Chase utilized to capture the woman's frothy garment, which contrast with the bolder, more broadly painted strokes used to model her head. The rapid strokes in the garment activate the composition, while the broad strokes in her face draw the viewer's attention directly to the artist's subject. A careful balance between the two is achieved by the placement of the woman's hand and arm, delicately supporting her head and unifying the composition. This pose of hand to face, suggesting pensiveness, is one that Chase used in several of his most successful portraits of women. Unlike a lesser artist who might take this simple device and use it as a formula, Chase used it only as one means of indicating feminine intelligence and dignity. Addressing the character of each of his sitters, he varied the mood of each work to reflect their individual personalities. He achieved this by modifying the expression and the directness and intensity of the gaze of each.

One of the earliest of these paintings is *Portrait of Miss Dora Wheeler*, 1883 (Cleveland Museum of Art).

In this work Chase portrays an intelligent, serious woman who gazes at the viewer in a piercing, fixed manner—an imposing, almost intimidating image. In contrast, Chase utilizes a similar pose to create a very different mood in his pastel *Meditation*, 1885–1886 (private collection). Here the subject's thoughts are not direct and penetrating, but rather inward and contemplative, as indicated by the title. *Portrait of a Lady* portrays another woman engaged in thought. Her gaze is direct, but rather than being intimidating it is engaging, as Chase portrays a vivacious, animated young woman whose charm and wit might easily match that of the artist. In fact, one might sense in her bemusement that she is about to respond to some clever banter.

Although the identity of the sitter cannot be confirmed, she is evidently a woman Chase knew personally who posed for him on several occasions; she may be the model for *Portrait of Mrs. C. (Lady with a White Shawl)* (Pennsylvania Academy of the Fine Arts, Philadelphia) which was executed the same year. Unlike this large, full-length portrait that was intended to be a major exhibition piece, *Portrait of a Lady*, more quickly and naturally conceived and more spontaneously painted, is a personal statement, a candid and sensitive portrayal of a spirited young woman whose warmth and beauty appealed to the artist's sentiment.

Ronald G. Pisano

1. *Portrait of a Lady* may have been originally titled *The Fur Wrap*, a work listed in Wilbur David Peat, intro. "Checklist of Known Work by William M. Chase," in *Chase Centennial Exhibition*, exh. cat. (Indianapolis: John Herron Art Institute, 1949), oil on canvas, 21 × 17 inches, signed lower right, 1893; collection of Gladys Wiles (daughter of Irving Wiles and a student of Chase), Peconic, Long Island.
2. William Merritt Chase to A. Margaret Archambault, 16 March 1914, Archambault Collection, Archives of American Art, Smithsonian Institution, Washington, D.C.
3. Benjamin Northrop, "From a Talk by William M. Chase with Benjamin Northrop of the Mail and Express," *Art Amateur* 30 (February 1894): 77.

Thomas Wilmer Dewing (1851–1938)

8. *The Dance*, ca. 1920–1921

Pastel on paper
13⅞ × 10½ inches
Signed lower right: *T. W. Dewing/205*[1]

Provenance:
(Vose Gallery, Boston), by 1921
to Mr. Woods King, Cleveland, 1921
to (Gage Gallery, Cleveland)
Mrs. J. Cheever Cowdin, New York, as of 1962
(Davis Galleries, New York), 1962
(Mr. Robert Isaacson, New York), 1962-1969
(Davis Galleries, New York), 1969
to Mr. and Mrs. Ralph Spencer, 1970

Exhibited:
Durlacher Brothers, New York, *A Loan Exhibition: Thomas W. Dewing*, 26 March–20 April 1963, no. 28.

This work will be included in the forthcoming catalogue raisonné of the work of Thomas Dewing by Susan Hobbs.

ONE OF THOMAS WILMER DEWING'S finest late pastels, *The Dance* is remarkable in the artist's oeuvre for its relatively large size and for the unusual movement of the graceful, swaying figure. In rendering the subject, Dewing employs an essentially monochromatic tonality of mauve highlighted by suggestions of blue and green. He applies the pastel crayon in small, parallel strokes, drawing only the surfaces that are illuminated by light. Using the least possible means, Dewing does not indicate the shadows with pastel, but instead relies on the carmel-hued paper to indicate the range of transitional values in the delicate figure. Garbed in diaphanous chiffon, she seems to hover like an apparition—a vision at once impalpable and elegantly compelling.

In reviewing a small display of Dewing's pastels in 1926, critic Royal Cortissoz told viewers that Dewing's artistic purpose was not the achievement of sentiment or romance: "His purpose is higher than that . . . What he seeks to do is to invest his studies with the quality of beauty to put before us simply an impression of feminine loveliness."[2]

The Dance was executed late in 1920 or early in 1921, after which it was sold to Cleveland collector Woods King. Dewing was then embarking on a new phase of his career, during which he devoted himself almost entirely to the production of pastels, for he found oil painting too taxing and time consuming. Pastels, on the other hand, were very popular at the time, and Dewing felt impelled to meet the demand. Eventually a number of his pastels were shown in several small exhibitions. Although there is no concrete evidence to support the contention, it is likely that Dewing showed *The Dance* in these exhibitions, for it is one of his largest and most dramatic pastels.[3] In order to keep track of these diminutive essays in color, in about 1910 Dewing began to place a number below his signature, such as we see on this work.[4]

Dewing first began to use the medium during the early 1890s, after he had seen Whistler's pastels in the collection of his patron Charles Lang Freer. Whistler was famed for employing one predominate hue in his tiny drawings. Dewing went on to develop this monochromatic aesthetic in his own unique fashion. The subject in *The Dance*, for example, is so reduced in color that the figure seems to be defined by light itself. Strongly illuminated from the left, she steps forward from a dark background provided by the rich hues of the contrasting paper. Unlike the vast majority of Dewing's pastels, which are relatively static and

immobile, the subject here is vital and animated. She moves daintily towards the viewer, holding out the gossamer folds of her dress. The artist had first treated dancing figures during the 1890s, when he framed them against verdant foliage in a number of large landscape oils. There he employed the diminutive feminine form as an emblem of grace and elegance. Dewing returned to the dance theme nearly twenty years later both in this pastel and in a landscape painting called *May*, 1921 (private collection, Massachusetts). In both works, his figures sway in a lyrical dance, moving to the strains of music that they alone can hear.

Susan Hobbs

1. Indicates the number recorded in Dewing's Private Record Book (private collection) for this work.
2. Royal Cortissoz, "Some Exquisite Pastels by an American Artist," *New York Herald Tribune*, 23 May 1926, p. 7.
3. From 16 December 1923 to 20 January 1924, the Corcoran Gallery, Washington, D.C. staged an exhibition of Dewing's pastels and silverpoints, as did Milch Galleries, New York, in May 1926.
4. Dewing explains his use of numbers in lieu of titles for the pastels, in a letter to C. Powell Minnigerode, Director of the Corcoran Gallery of Art. See T. W. Dewing to C. Powell Minnigerode, T. W. Dewing File, Archives, Corcoran Gallery of Art, Washington, D.C.

Arthur Burdett Frost, Sr. (1851–1928)

9. *Sparrows in the Snow*, ca. 1880s–1890s

Watercolor on paper
13½ × 11 inches
Signed lower left: *A. B. Frost*

Provenance:
Oscar Rudolph, New York
(Spanierman Gallery, New York), as of 1965
to Mr. and Mrs. Ralph Spencer, 1965

RECOGNIZED AT THE turn of the century as the "dean of American illustrators," Arthur B. Frost was also an accomplished easel painter, specializing in sporting and wildlife subjects.[1] A native of Philadelphia, Frost became apprenticed to a local wood engraver at the age of fifteen. In 1874, while working as a lithographer, he was invited to illustrate Max Adeler's *Out of the Hurly Burly*.[2] His drawings for this book were widely acclaimed by the critics and subsequently brought his work to the attention of the periodical press. Throughout the next five decades, Frost's illustrations graced the pages of many important magazines, including *Harper's*, *Scribner's*, *Life*, *Collier's*, and the *Canadian Illustrated News*. He was especially admired for his ability to portray his characters, especially rural types and farm animals, with a sympathetic yet discerning humor. Frost also illustrated numerous books by such noted authors as Mark Twain, Joel Chandler Harris, and Charles Dickens.

Despite his celebrity in the field of illustration, Frost was desirous of attaining recognition as a serious painter. To refine his skills, he attended classes at the Pennsylvania Academy of the Fine Arts from 1878 to 1881. Under the tutelage of Thomas Eakins, who became a close friend, Frost developed a realist style, emphasizing the tenets of firm draftsmanship and sound composition. During 1891 he took further instruction from William Merritt Chase, both in New York and in Shinnecock Hills, Long Island. Writing to his friend and fellow artist Augustus Daggy, Frost predicted that Chase would teach him to "loosen up my blamed tight fist, and get some go into my work."[3] Frost would later alternate styles in accordance with his subject matter, moving between a conventional, academic manner and a freer, Impressionist-inspired approach. Although color-blind, he possessed an acute sense of value and tone.

In 1906 Frost and his family went to Paris, where he hoped to further his development as a painter. Assuming they would follow in his footsteps, he enrolled his two sons, Arthur, Jr. (1887–1917) and John (1890–1937), at the Académie Julian. A staunch traditionalist, Frost remained devoted to sound draftsmanship and a realistic conception of nature; he was greatly distressed when Arthur, Jr. assimilated the principles of European modernism and became a pioneering figure in American abstraction.

Working in both oil and watercolor, Frost painted landscapes, still lifes, and genre scenes. However, he was best known for his depictions of North American sporting and wildlife themes. Frost became involved in this type of iconography as early as 1876, when *Harper's Weekly* hired him to provide drawings for articles on hunting, fishing, and other outdoor sporting pursuits. His enduring concern for indigenous wildlife is well exemplified in *Sparrows in the Snow*. This watercolor study features six small birds nestled within a universal field of white tinged here and there with subtle tones of gray. The work may date from the 1880s, when Frost resided in Philadelphia and, later, West Conshohocken, Pennsylvania, or from the 1890s, when he purchased an old mansion called "Moneysunk" in Convent Station, New Jersey.[4]

While much of Frost's illustration work was executed in pen and ink, he was "personally happiest when he could relax in the looser medium of watercolor."[5] Using a fluid yet highly controlled brushstroke, Frost has accurately captured the birds' characteristic postures as well as their distinctive, monochromatic coloration. Nestled against the blanket of snow, their wings tucked in tightly to retain warmth, they appear as dark, softly mottled masses of feather and down, delicately rendered in shades of brown and gray with touches of white and black. Certainly, *Sparrows in the Snow* is based on the artist's direct observation of nature; yet, at the same time, Frost has imbued his composition with the artistic sensitivity and honest simplicity that characterized his productions in all media.

Carol Lowrey

1. "A. B. Frost," *New York Evening Post*, 26 June 1928, p. 14.
2. Max Adeler was the pseudonym used by Charles Herber Clarke.
3. A. B. Frost to Augustus S. Daggy, 1891, cited in Henry M. Reed, *The World of A.B. Frost: His Family and Their Circle*, exh. cat. (Montclair, N.J.: Montclair Art Museum, 1983), p. 6.
4. Frost lived in Convent Station from 1890 until 1906 and again from 1916 until 1919. In 1923, after spending several years in Pennsylvania, he settled in Pasadena, California, remaining there for the rest of his life.
5. "Noted Frost Enters Cleveland Collection," *Art Digest* 14 (1 December 1939): 21.

George Overbury "Pop" Hart (1868–1933)

10. *Bathing Beach*, 1921

Watercolor and pencil on paper
14 × 22 inches
Signed and dated lower left: *Hart/Int. Park 1921*

Provenance:
(Marie Sterner)
Lawrence Rill Schumann Art Foundation, Boston
(Spanierman Gallery, New York), 1970s
to Mr. and Mrs. Ralph Spencer, 1970s

DURING A CAREER that extended from the 1890s to his death in 1933, George Overbury "Pop" Hart participated in a variety of artistic movements. He has most often been associated with the New York Realist and American Scene movements, but he also experimented with Impressionist and Post-Impressionist aesthetics. He is noted, too, for his artistic expeditions to such exotic locales as Tahiti, North Africa, the West Indies, and Mexico. Although many writers have perpetuated the myth that Hart was a naive, untrained artist, he actually attended the School of the Art Institute of Chicago from 1894 to 1897 and studied for a brief period in 1907 at the Académie Julian in Paris. During the 1910s and 1920s, Hart was a central figure in the artists' colony based in Fort Lee, New Jersey, and he counted among his close associates such renowned figures as Arthur B. Davies, Walt Kuhn, Jules Pascin, and Edward Hopper.[1]

William H. Gerdts has noted that within "a realistic sometimes reportorial style, Hart was perhaps America's finest watercolorist . . . combining brilliant draftsmanship with broad free-flowing washes of color."[2] While Hart had received formal training in art, he was never drawn to the slavish methods of academic oil painting. He prized spontaneity and graphic immediacy in his art, and thus preferred to work in such media as drawing, printmaking, and watercolor. Hart's frequent travels and his penchant for working *en plein air* also required the use of portable materials like pastel and watercolor.

Hart's expressive approach to watercolor has been seen as part of the stylistic revolution in American watercolor painting that had been initiated by Winslow Homer and John Singer Sargent. However, Hart can be viewed more accurately as an heir to this tradition, as he sought to expand upon the technical and stylistic premises of the older artists' work. Like Homer and Sargent, Hart used an energetic, improvisational painting technique, but he employed it with an even more daring modernist freedom. In many of his watercolors of the 1910s and 1920s, Hart utilized a fairly radical method of layering paint in loose, watery strokes, allowing his passages to drip and blend together in an accidental manner. During his own day, Hart, along with John Marin and Charles Burchfield, was regarded as a leading figure in American watercolor painting, and scholars have since singled out the value of his efforts to advance and enrich the technical potential of the medium.

Bathing Beach is a fine example of Hart's innovative watercolor technique, and its subject is also quite typical of the anecdotal, realist themes he favored. During the 1910s, he was associated with various members of the New York Realist circle, like Jerome Myers, Robert Henri, and John Sloan. Inspired by the realist credo of Henri and Sloan, Hart took a keen interest in casually rendered depictions of everyday life. This scene of strolling, picnicking figures was executed along the beach front of Coytesville, New Jersey, where Hart had his studio. (This subject undoubtedly held a particular appeal for Hart, since he later used it as the basis for his 1925 print *Bathing Beach, Coytesville on Hudson*.) Using rapid jottings of charcoal and splotches of paint, Hart was able to capture the marine atmosphere and the fleeting movement of the milling bathers. *Bathing Beach* also contains a rich mixture of coloristic and textural effects, created by combining translucent washes with chalky, opaque layers of pigment. Moreover, the style of this piece reflects Hart's debt to Maurice Prendergast, as can be seen in the jewellike touches of color and the transformation of figures into abstracted, ideographic swirls of paint. *Bathing Beach* represents "Pop" Hart's ambition to synthesize in his work a progressive aesthetic with a sensitive observation of regional life.

Gregory Gilbert

1. William H. Gerdts, Jr., *Painting and Sculpture in New Jersey*, New Jersey Historical Series, vol. 21 (Princeton, N.J.: D. Van Nostrand Co., 1964), p. 211.
2. Gerdts, p. 200. For additional references to Hart's watercolors, see Gregory Gilbert, *George Overbury "Pop" Hart: His Life and Art* (New Brunswick, N.J.: Rutgers University Press, 1986), pp. 46–50; Christopher Finch, *American Watercolors* (New York: Abbeville Press, 1986), p. 244; Theodore E. Stebbins, Jr., *American Master Drawings and Watercolors on Paper from Colonial Times to the Present* (New York: Harper and Row, 1976), p. 297.

Childe Hassam (1859–1935)

II. *Les Buttes, Montmartre, July 14, 1889*

Oil on canvas
11½ × 10½ inches
Signed and dated lower left: *Childe Hassam 1889*

Provenance:
(Macbeth Gallery, New York)
Ruth and Albert E. McVitty
Estate of Ruth McVitty, Princeton, New Jersey
to (Spanierman Gallery, New York), as of 1969
to Mr. and Mrs. Ralph Spencer, 1969

Exhibited:
Metropolitan Museum of Art, New York, *Childe Hassam as Printmaker: A Selection in Various Media*, 28 June 1977–11 September 1977, no. 32.

This work will be included in the forthcoming catalogue raisonné of the work of Childe Hassam, now in preparation by Stuart P. Feld and Kathleen M. Burnside.

CHILDE HASSAM was already a recognized illustrator and watercolorist when he departed Boston for Paris late in 1886. During his three-year sojourn he was fascinated by the variety of bustling streetlife in the French capital, and his work of the period ranges from small-scale urban glimpses rapidly executed in oil or watercolor to fully developed Salon canvases, such as the prize-winning *Jour du Grand Prix*, 1887 (New Britain [Conn.] Museum of American Art).[1]

Painted near the end of his stay in Paris, *Les Buttes, Montmartre* reveals Hassam's previous American training, for the picture is quite graphic: Hassam builds the composition on a hard-edged diagonal wedge of cobbled street and masonry wall, counterpoised by the softer, undulant line of the green buttes. Judiciously scattered figures balance the colorful flags that fill the upper third of the canvas.

Yet by 1889, when *Montmartre* was painted, Hassam had begun to soften his technique, absorbing and synthesizing the lessons of French Impressionism, as exemplified by Claude Monet.[2] Hassam's palette was lightening, and sculptural volumes were giving way to flattened shapes. His earlier American street scenes, such as *Rainy Day, Boston*, 1885 (Toledo Museum of Art, Ohio), as well as some of the works he painted in Paris in the late 1880s, such as, *Une Averse, Rue Bonaparte*, 1887 (private collection), were sober and gray, but works like *Montmartre* are filled with effects of sunlight and fresh air that add sparkle and presage his Impressionist landscapes of the ensuing two decades. Like many of his Parisian street scenes, *Montmartre* is small in scale, and the picture's square format marks Hassam as a progressive young modern artist, interested in aesthetic issues that stand apart from subject matter.

Nonetheless, the picture's subject is not without importance or interest. Hassam visited a narrow little street located on what were still the northern outskirts of Paris. By the 1890s, Montmartre would gain notoriety as a wild quarter frequented by artists and entertainers, as captured in the paintings of Henri de Toulouse-Lautrec and others. But Hassam's gentle streetscape hints at neither approaching urban development nor bohemian impropriety. Rather, Hassam's work is close in spirit to the idyllic scenes of working-class recreation painted in Montmartre by Auguste Renoir, who had rented a studio in the neighborhood by 1876.[3] Like Renoir's Montmartre subjects—seamstresses, florists, and milliners— Hassam's women are not the fashionably dressed ladies who frequented the broad boulevards and elegant parks of the post-Haussmann French captial. At the edge of the city, where urban and rural overlap, Hassam's women wear clean aprons and carry large market baskets.

In contrast to the somber, solid, black-and-white forms of the figures, the French tricolor creates a series of colorful flat bars: red, white, and blue. The canvas depicts a July 14 celebration, painted on the hundredth anniversary of the fall of the Bastille (1789) and the start of the Revolution. On the centennial of political upheaval, these women in traditional, unpretentious costumes evoke the stability of country ways. As the Bastille symbolized despotism and economic hardship during the final years of Louis XVI's rule, Hassam appropriately depicted common folk, rather than sophisticated city dwellers, enjoying their holiday. The colorful French flags that caught Hassam's eye as a visually acute tourist anticipate by a quarter of a century his extended series of American flags, painted as a frankly patriotic response to the events of World War I.[4]

David Park Curry

1. This painting won a gold medal in the Salon of 1888.
2. Hassam had ample opportunity to see Monet's work in both Boston and Paris, although there is no evidence that the two artists ever met. In June 1889, just before Hassam painted *Les Buttes, Montmartre*, Monet exhibited one of his earlier flag paintings, *La Rue Montorgueil, Fête du 30 Juin 1878*, an oil of 1878, at the Georges Petit Gallery in Paris. Hassam is also known to have exhibited there in 1889. See Daniel Wildenstien, *Claude Monet, Biographie et catalogue raisonné*, vol. 1 (Lausanne and Paris: La Bibliothèque des Arts, 1974), p. 316, no. 469.
3. Robert Herbert has discussed Renoir's *Dance at the Moulin de la Galette*, 1876 (Musée d'Orsay, Paris) as a semi-urban fête galante. See Robert L. Herbert, *Impressionism: Art, Leisure, and Parisian Society* (New Haven, Conn.: Yale University Press, 1988), pp. 136–139.
4. For a study of the American flag series, see Ilene Susan Fort, *The Flag Paintings of Childe Hassam*, exh. cat. (Los Angeles: Los Angeles County Museum of Art, 1988).

Childe Hassam

12. *The Altar and Shrine*, 1892

Watercolor on paper
15¾ × 12¼ inches
Signed and dated lower left: *Childe Hassam/1892*
Inscribed lower left: *Isles of Shoals*

Provenance:
Evelyn Benedict, Newport, Rhode Island
(Schweitzer Gallery, New York), as of 1967
to Mr. and Mrs. Ralph Spencer, 1967

Exhibited:
Whitney Museum of American Art, New York,
*Eighteenth and Nineteenth Century American Art
from Private Collections*, 1972, no. 32.
Whitney Museum of American Art, New York, *Turn-
of-the-Century America*, 30 June–2 October 1977
(p. 51 ill.). Circulating exhibition, 1977–1978.
Yale University Art Gallery, New Haven, Connecticut,
Childe Hassam: An Island Garden Revisited, 4
April–10 June 1990 (p. 47 col. ill.).

Literature:
Celia Thaxter, *An Island Garden* (Boston: Houghton,
Mifflin, 1894), opp. p. 94 chromolithograph ill.
David Park Curry, *Childe Hassam: An Island Garden
Revisited* (New York: W. W. Norton & Co., 1990),
pp. 43, 45–46, 47 col. ill.

This work will be included in the forthcoming
catalogue raisonné of the work of Childe Hassam
now in preparation by Stuart P. Feld and Kathleen
M. Burnside.

All summer long within this pleasant room
the flowers hold carnival in every possible
combination of beauty. All summer long it
is kept fresh and radiant with their
loveliness—a wonder of bloom, color, and
fragrance. Year after year a long procession
of charming people come and go . . . and
the flowers that glow for their delight seem
to listen with them to the music that stirs
each blossom upon its stem.

Celia Thaxter, *An Island Garden* (1894)

AGAINST A GRIDWORK of framed
pictures, a roseate cloud of poppies, ranging
from dazzling white to deep maroon, is banked
atop a bookcase in *The Altar and Shrine*, an accomplished watercolor by Childe Hassam. Two tables
laden with flower-filled vases flank the bookcase, and
the artist has crowded and overlapped bits of art and
nature to suggest that this was not an ordinary room.

Poet and journalist Celia Laighton Thaxter (1835–
1894) called this spot in her parlor the "altar and
shrine." Here she celebrated progressive art, literature,
and music in an atmosphere of exalted natural beauty.
A lighthouse keeper's daughter, Thaxter was herself an
aesthetic beacon, attracting important nineteenth-
century artists, writers, and musicians to her famous
salon at Appledore, on the Isles of Shoals, a group of
rocky outcroppings ten miles off the New Hampshire
coast.

When Hassam began frequenting Thaxter's salon,
in the mid-1880s, he was just establishing his
reputation as a watercolorist. On the strength of his
skill in this medium, Thaxter invited him to illustrate
An Island Garden (1894), her last book. *The Altar and
Shrine* is one of two parlor scenes to appear. Most of
Hassam's full-page illustrations record views of her
garden and the rocky landscape beyond it, while floral
vignettes scattered across the book's pages reproduce
blossoms cultivated by the poet.[2]

Although the cottage and its contents were
destroyed by fire in 1914, written descriptions survive.
Thaxter wrote that the room was

made first for music. . . . There are no
heavy draperies . . . nothing to absorb the
sound. The piano stands midway at one
side; there are couches, sofas with pillows
. . . mostly of warm shades of green. There
are low bookcases round the walls. . . . The

high walls to the ceiling are covered with
pictures, and flowers are everywhere.[3]

In *The Altar and Shrine* Hassam captured the
type of interior Henry James called a "cushioned
feminine nest." The room was festooned with
paintings, prints, and drawings, "pinned up against the
parlor wall, which was like a wondrous scrapbook."
The Altar and Shrine obscures obvious reference to
Hassam's own art, but an old photograph of the spot
reveals one of his lighthouse watercolors on display.
The pastel on the table and a seascape over the mantle,
partly hidden by the lavish arrangement of poppies
might be by Hassam as well.

Hassam's keenest interest was reserved for the
flowers, and his few Appledore interiors dwell on
masses of cut blossoms that made the room seem "like
living in a rainbow."[5]

Hassam's frontal composition gives *The Altar and
Shrine* the impact of an icon. As resident priestess,
Thaxter decorated the spot "almost as one would paint
a picture or compose a sonata."[6] The cross-fertilization
of art, music, and literature help to account for the
power of Hassam's work at the Shoals. Like the finest
outdoor images created there, *The Altar and Shrine* is
energized by the artist's sensuous embrace of light and
color effects, but at the same time it reveals his
determination to maintain a balanced synthesis
between line and color. A century after its creation,
The Altar and Shrine retains its fresh beauty, a graceful
and touching memory of a now-lost summer place.

David Park Curry

1. During the mid-1880s Hassam served as Celia Thaxter's substitute
watercolor teacher. Eventually their friendship culminated in
publication of *An Island Garden* (Boston: Houghton, Mifflin, 1894;
facsimile ed., 1988), which is richly illustrated with chromolithographs
all taken after Shoals images by Hassam.
2. *A Favorite Corner*, a watercolor of 1892 (private collection), shows a
close-up view of a flower-laden table, and was the second interior
image in *An Island Garden*. There is a major oil of Thaxter's parlor,
The Room of Flowers, 1894 (Altschul Collection, New York). Given
that Hassam created approximately 4000 works over his long career,
and that ten percent depict the Isles of Shoals, the three known Shoals
interiors are extremely rare.
3. Thaxter, *An Island Garden*, pp. 93–94. Thaxter goes on to describe
the scene depicted in *The Altar and Shrine* at length.
4. Celia Thaxter, Appledore to Annie Fields [location unknown], 4
May 1869, cited in Annie Fields and Rose Lamb, eds., *Letters of Celia
Thaxter* (Boston: Houghton, Mifflin, 1895), p. 141.
5. Candace Wheeler, *Content in a Garden* (Boston: Houghton, Mifflin,
1901), p. 57.
6. Maud Appleton McDowell, cited in Celia Thaxter, *The Heavenly
Guest, with Other Unpublished Writings*, ed. Oscar Laighton
(Andover, Mass.: Smith & Contts, Printers, 1935), pp. 137–138.

Charles Hawthorne (1872–1930)

13. *Girl with a Vase*, ca. 1910

Oil on canvas
30 × 25 inches
Signed upper left: *C. W. Hawthorne*

Provenance:
(Macbeth Galleries, New York)
(Babcock Galleries, New York), as of 1966
to Mr. and Mrs. Ralph Spencer, 1966

CHARLES HAWTHORNE, whose poignant images of the rugged seafaring families of Cape Cod rank him among the major realists of the early twentieth century, was born in Lodi, Illinois, in 1872. The son of a sea captain, he grew up in the coastal town of Richmond, Maine.

In 1890 the young Hawthorne ventured to New York, where he worked on the docks and, later, in a stained glass factory, in order to support evening classes at the Art Students League under George de Forest Brush, Frank DuMond, and Henry Siddons Mowbray. The summer of 1896 found the artist in Shinnecock, Long Island, at the school of William Merritt Chase. Soon he became Chase's assistant, and in the fall, he helped to organize the Chase School in Manhattan. A summer in Zandvoort, Holland, followed. Influenced by the genre work of Frans Hals, Hawthorne painted the villagers, the fisherfolk, and the unfortunates of the Dutch community's poorhouse.

Similar subjects awaited the artist in Provincetown, Massachusetts, where he settled after his return to America in 1898. The next year, Hawthorne established his own school, the Cape Cod School of Art, which flourished under his direction for the next three decades. Provincetown in the 1890s was an unspoiled fishing village whose hearty inhabitants of Yankee and Portuguese stock were immortalized by Hawthorne in early works such as *Cleaning Fish*, 1899 (location unknown), *Splitting Fish*, 1903 (Town of Provincetown), and *Man With Oar*, 1905 (location unknown). In these, he combined the bravura style he had gleaned from Hals and Chase to capture the character and verve of the local people.

A new style emerged around 1906, when several patrons, including the noted collector John Gellatly, provided the artist with funds for a two-year stay in Italy. Deeply impressed by the Renaissance masters Giorgione, Perugino, and especially Titian, Hawthorne returned to his Provincetown themes with a new interest in simplified design and technique. (He subsequently developed a method of underpainting with tempera and a special pigment, manufactured under the name "Hawthorne's medium.") He also began to treat his figural subjects with a deeper sensitivity to their psychological makeup. The works that followed, including the masterful *Trousseau*, 1910 (Metropolitan Museum of Art, New York), *The Family*, 1911 (Albright-Knox Art Gallery, Buffalo), and *The Widow* (location unknown), conflate Old Master tendencies with this new approach, winning for the artist national recognition and representation in fourteen museum collections by the age of forty.[1]

Hawthorne was especially successful in portraying youth. The transition from girlhood to womanhood was profoundly expressed in *The Trousseau*, and in *Girl with Vase*, a work of the same period, he pursues a similar theme. The bold, simplified shape of the young woman's figure nearly fills the visual field, heightening the impact of her presence. The only adornments to her simple blue dress are the rose-colored waist sash and a strand of pearls, its soft curve echoing the roundness of her face and form. One extended arm holds a nosegay of sweet william, the flower shown in the vase and an obvious reference to the maturing beauty of the woman herself. It is the face, however, that clearly holds the viewer's attention. Absorbed in her private world, she gazes out in an expression reviewers called the "Hawthorne stare." The noted critic and collector Duncan Phillips understood this aspect of Hawthorne's work:

> It is Youth which appeals most keenly to this artist. The freshness and wistfulness of maidenhood have won from Hawthorne many a graceful tribute. The unspoken thought interested the poet in him. . . . Hawthorne's models have thus been given universal significance as symbols for us all. They symbolize our obscure play-acting, all unconscious of the stage we tread, of the little dramas of our lonely destinies.[2]

In *Girl with Vase* Hawthorne captures the wondrous joy and also the apprehension of young womanhood, transposing an everyday theme into one of universal significance.

Laurene Buckley

1. Hawthorne is represented in major institutions, including The Metropolitan Museum of Art, New York; The Brooklyn Museum, New York; The Carnegie Museum of Art, Pittsburgh; The Corcoran Gallery of Art, Washington, D.C.; Museum of Fine Arts, Boston; The Art Institute of Chicago; National Academy of Design, New York as well as numerous private collections.
2. Duncan Phillips, "Charles W. Hawthorne," *International Studio* 61 (March 1917): xxii.

Robert Henri (1865–1929)

14. *On the Marne*, 1899

Oil on canvas
26 × 32 inches
Signed lower right: *Robert Henri*
Inscribed verso: *Robert Henri/The River Bank/30/A/2*[1]

Provenance:
Estate of Robert Henri
Estate of Mrs. Robert Henri, as of 1931
Miss Violet Organ, New York, the artist's sister-in-law, as of 1937–1954
to (Hirschl & Adler Galleries, New York), 1954–1967
to Mr. and Mrs. Ralph Spencer, 1967

Exhibited:
Metropolitan Museum of Art, New York, *The Robert Henri Memorial Exhibition*, 9 March–19 April 1931, no. 3 (ill.) (lent by Estate of Mrs. Robert Henri).
Whitney Museum of American Art, New York, *New York Realists, 1900–1914*, 9 February–5 March 1937, no. 27 (lent by Miss Violet Organ, New York).
Hirschl & Adler Galleries, New York, *Robert Henri, Fifty Paintings*, 3–28 February 1958, no. 7.
Hirschl & Adler Galleries, New York, *Retrospective of a Gallery: Twenty Years*, 8 November-1 December 1973, no. 55 (ill.).
Delaware Art Museum, Wilmington, *Robert Henri: Painter*, 4 May–24 June 1984, no. 22 (pp. 52 ill., 53). Circulating exhibition, 1984–1985.

Literature:
Bennard B. Perlman, *Painters of the Ashcan School: The Immortal Eight*, reprint (New York: Dover Publications, 1988), p. 74 ill.

ROBERT HENRI, one of the leading members of the Eight, is best known for his vigorously brushed portraits and New York cityscapes from just after the turn of the century, images of bold chiaroscuro that challenged the academic establishment. However, during the past twenty years, more and more recognition has been given to Henri's work of the 1890s. The decade was much more than a period of apprenticeship for his later urban realism: it was a time when he reached artistic maturity in scores of thoughtfully designed paintings, executed mostly in France, that reveal his sensitive, poetic response to his environment. One of these is *On the Marne*, also known as *The River Bank*, which was painted at Alfort, a suburb southeast of Paris where his painter friend Edward Redfield had established himself with his family.

Henri portrays, in the left foreground, a houseboat moored on the banks of the River Marne. Adjoining it are several skiffs or rowboats, perhaps waiting to be rented by Parisians on a holiday outing. From this point, we are invited to follow the river bank meandering slowly into the distance at the right. Behind and above the shore is a gently sloping meadow, closed off in the far distance by a densely foliated row of trees.

Henri shows us a particular place, but he is not burdened by detail. His strokes are broad and general, portraying his subject in balanced masses of tone, a subdued but not a depressing effect. In his palette of deep greens, olives, tans, and ochers, he shows his allegiance to Gustave Courbet, the Barbizon School, and the early work of Edouard Manet. At this point in his career he had abandoned the bright, scintillating hues of Impressionism, which had fascinated him briefly earlier in the decade, and had committed himself to a darker, tonal style. Although this became the foundation for his pictorial language after 1900, identified with New York Realism, it was practiced here without his later self-conscious bravado and gusto.

For Henri, the last two years of the decade, spent in and near Paris, were a time of growing confidence and accomplishment. In 1899 he had painted his celebrated *La Neige*, a snowy Parisian street scene, and in that year it was purchased by the Luxembourg Museum in Paris, a signal honor for the thirty-four-year old American. *On the Marne* was also executed in 1899, probably after *La Neige*, and shares with that work an admirable command of composition, tone, and drawing.

William Innes Homer

1. In the Henri Record Books (Estate of Robert Henri), *On the Marne* carries the designation 30/A/2 signifying that it is listed in Book A, p. 30, the second item on that page.

John La Farge (1835–1910)

15. *Hollyhocks*, ca. 1879–1885

Watercolor and gouache on paper
16⅜ × 14½ inches

Provenance:
Mrs. Samuel Parkman Blake, by 1910
to Marian L. Blake, Boston, Mrs. Parkman Blake's
    daughter, 1935
to (Castano Gallery, Boston), by 1958
to (Hirschl & Adler Galleries, New York), 1958–1961
to Lawrence A. and Barbara Fleischman, Detroit and
    New York, 1961–1967
to (Hirschl & Adler Galleries, New York), 1967
to Mr. and Mrs. Ralph Spencer, 1967

Exhibited:
Museum of Fine Arts, Boston, *La Farge Memorial
    Exhibition*, January 1911, (lent by Mrs. S. Parkman
    Blake).
Hirschl & Adler Galleries, New York, *American
    Paintings for Public and Private Collections*, 4
    December 1967–13 January 1968, no. 67.
A. C. A. Galleries, New York, *American Flower
    Painting, 1850–1950*, 1–22 April 1978.

Literature:
Kathleen A. Foster, "The Still-Life Paintings of John
    La Farge," *American Art Journal* 11 (July 1979):
    36 ill.

This work will be included in the *Catalogue Raisonné
of the Works of John La Farge: Volume 1, Oils and
Watercolors* by Henry A. La Farge, James L.
Yarnall, and Mary A. La Farge (New Haven,
Conn.: Yale University Press, forthcoming).

JOHN LA FARGE was a versatile artist whose work spanned a wide range of subject matter, styles, and media. The late 1870s marked a turning point in his career: he abandoned an early predilection for oil painting, turning his attention to decorative work and watercolor. As a decorator, La Farge gained renown for innovation in both stained glass and mural design. As a watercolorist, he assumed a role as a primary figure in the American watercolor movement.[1]

In late 1878 La Farge began to paint floral watercolors that garnered the kind of praise any artist would envy. In 1884, one critic noted: "No nearer approach has, probably, ever been made to the freshness, purity, and delicacy of texture of natural flowers. . . . it is on these modest watercolors that his fame, in the future, promises to rest."[2]

These watercolors were also lucrative and provided much needed income during a period of great financial distress for La Farge. "Mr. La Farge can no longer use his noble boast that he has never sold a picture from an exhibition," observed a critic in 1879. "The yellow ticket has found out the corners of his small and modest frames, and the artist can congratulate himself in having sold his pictures at full prices without concessions, and on having a mercantile success with a group of works in New York."[3]

In society circles of Boston and New York, the ownership of a La Farge still life became a status symbol. The artist's friends and colleagues avidly sought out these works, often purchasing them directly from La Farge before they could be offered for public sale.

From his earliest days as an artist, La Farge delighted in rendering the hollyhock.[4] Its bright contrasts of color and the sinuous intertwining of stems and leaves suited the moody expressiveness of his work. After 1879, the artist seized upon the decorative possibilities of the motif, adapting it to his vividly colored stained glass on a dozen occasions.[5] *Hollyhocks* is one of several watercolor studies of the flower executed at this time.

Hollyhocks is vigorously painted and gives the impression of a rapid sketch. Two white blossoms emerging from a swath of verdant leaves stand out against a pale gray sky. At the lower left, a delicate pink blossom provides a harmonious accent of bright color. The sensual floral forms are sketched with a calligraphic touch that evokes the calculated handling of Japanese ink painting. The broad washes of broken color are reminiscent of effects in La Farge's stained-glass windows. *Hollyhocks* is powerfully expressive and yet understated, and displays the best qualities of a peak period of La Farge's production as a watercolorist.

James L. Yarnall

1. See Kathleen A. Foster, "John La Farge and the American Watercolor Movement: Art for the 'Decorative Age,'" in *John La Farge*, exh. cat. (New York: Abbeville Press for the Carnegie Museum, Pittsburgh, and the National Museum of American Art, Washington, D.C., 1987), pp. 123–160.
2. Robert Jarvis, "Pictures by La Farge and Inness," *Art Amateur* 11 (June 1884): 12.
3. Earl Shinn, "The Growing School of American Water-Color Art," *Nation* 28 (6 March 1879): 172. Shinn was commenting on La Farge's successful sale of several works in the annual exhibition of the Society of American Painters in Watercolor, held in New York in March 1879.
4. La Farge took up the profession of art in 1859 in Newport, Rhode Island. He remained there throughout the 1860s and early 1870s, working largely on his own. His earliest studies of hollyhocks are sketchbook drawings (Yale University Art Gallery, New Haven), dating around 1863. In 1863, he painted a large oil of hollyhocks (private collection) that was widely exhibited and highly regarded, along with several smaller oils of the subject.
5. The windows in question were in the Frederick Lothrop Ames house, Boston (now in the St. Louis Art Museum); J. Pierrepont Morgan house, New York (evidently now lost); Michael Jenkins house, Baltimore (now privately owned); and Judge Thomas Grover house, Canton, Massachusetts (now in the Pennsylvania Academy of the Fine Arts, Philadelphia). A hollyhocks window (now lost) was also among the pieces exhibited by La Farge at the Paris Universal Exposition of 1889, where he received a gold medal and the French Legion of Honor for his glass.

Alfred H. Maurer (1868–1932)

16. *Still Life with Peonies*, 1926

Watercolor, gouache, and charcoal on paper
20½ × 18 inches
Signed and dated upper right: *A. H. Maurer/26*

Provenance:
Mrs. Montgomery Sears, Boston
Mrs. J. D. Cameron Bradley
  to (Parke Bernet, New York, 10–11 December 1947
    no. 112)
(Bertha Schaefer, New York), as of 1949
(Kraushaar Galleries, New York), as of 1969
  to Mr. and Mrs. Ralph Spencer, 1969

WRITING TO THE critic Carl Zigrosser, on June 17, 1926, from his summer boarding house in Marlboro, New York, Alfred H. Maurer cheerfully announced, "Started at flowers, having a good time."[1] At the age of fifty-eight, after nearly a decade of meager attention from dealers and critics alike, Maurer had reason to feel optimistic. Two years earlier, the gallery owner E. Weyhe had enthusiastically bought up the contents of his studio. Weyhe also promised to show the work of the prolific and marvelously adept, albeit quixotic, painter on a regular basis. Near the unfortunate end of his life (the artist hanged himself in 1932), Maurer was once again thrust into the headlines of the art pages of newspapers and magazines.[2]

At the turn of the century, a young Maurer had returned to New York from three years in Paris and won a gold medal from the Carnegie Institute International exhibition for a dashing Whistlerian figure study. In 1909 he had shocked conservative New Yorkers, including his father, who had been a Currier & Ives printmaker, with a group of fiery, boldly patterned landscapes shown at Alfred Stieglitz's 291 gallery. Forty years old at the time, Maurer was the best known American artist to adopt Fauvism, after direct contact with Henri Matisse. Returning to the United States from France at the outbreak of World War I, Maurer then languished professionally until the appearance of Mr. Weyhe at his door.

The feelings of renewal and rejuvenation Maurer experienced in the mid-1920s are registered most vividly in his return to still life, a genre he first investigated during his years abroad, under the influence of Paul Cézanne and Matisse. In *Still Life with Peonies*, a ceramic vase, placed on a pedestal like an icon, is overflowing with blossoming flowers and sprays of green. An opulent, abstract pattern of red, blue, yellow, and green swirls animates the atmosphere around the floral arrangement with palpable nervous energy. Here Maurer exploits the capabilities of watercolor to the fullest, capturing the nuances of emotion without losing control to the fluidity of the medium. Beneath the exuberance and vitality, one is aware of a truly masterful touch. In their expressionist finish and scintillating hue, reminiscent of Fauvism, Maurer's bouquets were unique and original works for the period. While other artists, including Charles Demuth, Georgia O'Keeffe, and Charles Sheeler, were absorbed with the smooth, coolly rational Precisionist aesthetic, Maurer, in a burst of joyous creativity, explored a more personal, vibrant mode.

These late watercolors by Maurer were greatly admired when first exhibited, largely for the fresh and independent outlook they conveyed. The present example was probably included in Maurer's one-man show of January 1927 at Weyhe's gallery. "An almost mellow bloom illuminates Alfred Maurer's most recent paintings of flowers and green bits of fragrant forests," readers of the *New York Times* were appreciatively informed.

It is silly to say of a grown artist such as Alfred Maurer that he has "grown" in one or two years time; but it is impossible in his case to avoid the even worse cliché that he is "realizing" his powers to their fullest. The academician Alfred Maurer, who, when on the approved high-road to a conventional aesthetic success, was compared to Chase and picked as his only possible successor, has become Alfred Maurer, a great American artist, who stands alone.[3]

Apparently, Mrs. Montgomery Sears, the Boston patroness whose collection included works by Matisse, Cézanne, and Maurice Prendergast, agreed with this assessment of Maurer's stature, for she once owned this beautiful watercolor.[4]

Nic Madormo

1. Alfred H. Maurer, Marlboro, N. Y. to Carl Zigrosser, [New York], 17 June 1926, Elizabeth McCausland Papers, Archives of American Art, Smithsonian Insitution, Washington, D.C.
2. See Henry McBride, "'Third Floor Back' Story with Moral," *New York Herald*, 20 January 1924, sec. 7, p. 15.
3. L. K., "In New York Galleries," *New York Times*, 16 January 1927, sec. 7, p. 10.
4. See the note on verso of the photograph of this painting in the Elizabeth McCausland Papers.

Willard Metcalf (1858–1925)

17. *The Red Bridge*, ca. 1911–1912

Oil on canvas
26½ × 29½ inches
Signed lower left: *W. L. Metcalf*

Provenance:
(Milch Galleries, New York)
(A. C. A. Galleries, New York), as of 1968
to Mr. and Mrs. Ralph Spencer, 1968

Exhibited:
Montross Gallery, New York, *Fifteenth Annual
Exhibition of the Ten American Painters*,
15 March–6 April 1912, no. 14.
Art Institute of Chicago, *Twenty-fifth Annual
Exhibition of Painting and Sculpture by American
Artists*, 5 November–8 December 1912, no. 166.
Montclair Art Museum, New Jersey, *American
Paintings by "The Ten,"* 1 January–10 February
1946, no. 23.
Whitney Museum of American Art, New York,
*Eighteenth and Nineteenth Century American Art
from Private Collections*, 27 June–11 September
1972, no. 45.
Whitney Museum of American Art, New York, *Turn-
of-the-Century America*, 29 June–2 October 1977,
no. 7. Circulating exhibition, 1977–1978.

Literature:
Charles de Kay, "Fifteen Times Ten," *American Art
News* 10 (23 March 1912): 9.
Elizabeth de Veer, "Willard Metcalf in Cornish, New
Hamphire," *Antiques* 124 (November 1984): 1211
col. ill.
Elizabeth de Veer and Richard J. Boyle, *Sunlight and
Shadow: The Life and Art of Willard Metcalf* (New
York: Abbeville Press, 1987), pp. 158–159 col. ill.

This work will be included in the forthcoming
catalogue raisonné of the work of Willard Metcalf
by Elizabeth de Veer.

THE EARLY 1910s was an especially good period for Willard Metcalf, both personally and professionally. It was during this time that he executed *The Red Bridge*, which he showed at the fifteenth annual exhibition of the Ten American Painters in March 1912.

In the winter of 1911, Metcalf married for the second time, spending his honeymoon in the hills of Cornish, New Hampshire, at the home of his friend Charles Platt, a painter, etcher, and architect.[1] The Metcalfs stayed with the Platts until the spring; in the fall of that year their daughter, Rosalind, was born. Probably encouraged by Thomas Dewing, one of his colleagues in the Ten, and by Platt, Metcalf first visited Cornish in 1909; he would continue to do so until 1920. Indeed there are more known depictions of the Cornish landscape by Metcalf than by any other member of the Cornish artists' colony.[2] Metcalf was also unique in the colony as he usually chose to visit in winter—certainly a beautiful season in the area, as attested by the extraordinary number of canvases in which he captured its special qualities. Among these, *The Red Bridge* is one of the finest.

In 1911 Metcalf also had two successful exhibitions. He had both a solo show at the Montross Gallery in New York that subsequently traveled throughout the country and a two-man show with Childe Hassam at the Detroit Art Institute. The following year, at the fifteenth annual exhibition of the Ten, Metcalf displayed five works, including a silverpoint drawing of his new wife, Henriette, and the landscape *The Red Bridge*.

Critics' responses to Metcalf's submissions were generally favorable, citing both his affinity for the landscape and his considerable technical ability. "Two winter landscapes, 'The Red Bridge' and 'The River Road,' . . . [are] very true to the clear remorseless atmosphere of our climate," wrote Charles de Kay, the reviewer for *American Art News*.[3] The critic from the *Evening Post* observed that his landscapes "are rather freer and more open than some of his canvases seen earlier in the season."[4] "It is interesting," wrote another, "to see how steadfastly the sketch bears looking into . . . how full of the spirit of the man who knows his craft . . . his two landscapes carry conviction so smoothly and so completely that they seem like open windows giving upon the scenes represented. . . . Facility could no further go, nor could landscape be more truthful."[5] Like the poet Robert Frost (who was working on a farm near Derry, New Hampshire, when Metcalf came to Cornish), Metcalf had a strong feeling of empathy for the New England landscape and an unaffected, straightforward, and deceptively simple style of expressing it.

Metcalf was a direct painter, and *The Red Bridge* is painted directly, demonstrating his debt to Barbizon and Impressionist traditions, as well as to American Realism. *The Red Bridge* is handled with the assurance of an artist intimate with his subject. The clarity of the blue sky is reflected in the partially snow-covered river. The light tones of the river and sky contrast with the muddy brown of the Cornish hills. At the bottom of these is lodged a New England village, its buildings rendered in various tones of violet-gray and white. Extending toward the village is a little bridge, its structure painted Venetian red, over which two figures have crossed. The figures establish a sense of scale and bring the eye toward the distant town. There are flecks of the bridge's red in the cluster of buildings and, to a degree, in the hills beyond. Thus the reds, along with a subtle violet tone, seem to knit the picture together, creating a delicate balance throughout this "freer and more open" painting.

The Red Bridge is about the union of opposites, about harmony and contrast, open and closed form, all at the service of the artist's ideas about the Cornish landscape. It is for such works that Metcalf has been called the "poet laureate of the New England hills."

Richard J. Boyle

1. Metcalf's Cornish works are discussed at length in Elizabeth de Veer and Richard J. Boyle, *Sunlight and Shadow: The Life and Art of Willard Metcalf* (New York: Abbeville Press, 1987), pp. 102–148.
2. See John H. Dryfhout, "The Cornish Colony," in *A Circle of Friends: Art Colonies of Cornish and Dublin,* exh. cat. (Durham, N. H.: University Art Galleries, University of New Hampshire, 1985), pp. 39–40.
3. Charles de Kay, "Fifteen Times Ten," *American Art News* 10 (23 March 1912): 9.
4. "Art Notes," *New York Evening Post*, 15 March 1912, p. 7.
5. R[oyal] C[ortissoz], "Art Exhibitions," *New-York Daily Tribune*, 20 March 1912, p. 7.

Jane Peterson (1876–1965)

18. *Vedder's Fountain, Tiffany's Garden*, ca. 1910

Oil on canvas
40 × 30 inches
Signed lower right: *Jane Peterson*

Provenance:
(Robert Schoelkopf Gallery, New York), as of 1965
to Mr. and Mrs. Ralph Spencer, 1965

PRIMARILY KNOWN for her Impressionistic floral landscapes, Jane Peterson was born in Elgin, Illinois, in 1876. At an early age, she was given an aptitude test for artistic ability at the Art Institute of Chicago, the results of which encouraged her to enroll at the Pratt Institute in Brooklyn in 1895, where she studied under Arthur Wesley Dow. His principles of simplified design and color are evident in Peterson's early work and continued to influence her throughout her career.

After graduating from Pratt in 1901, Peterson became the Supervisor of Drawing for the public schools in Brooklyn. She continued her studies at the Art Students League in New York under Frank DuMond, Henry B. Snell, and Birge Harrison. In the fall of 1906, she taught briefly at the Maryland Institute's School of Art and Design in Baltimore before sailing for Europe the following year. After a tour of the artists' colonies along the Cornish coast, at Volendam, Holland, and Lake Como, Italy, Peterson decided to remain abroad for more artistic study. In London she worked with the English artist Frank Brangwyn, whose bold sense of design helped shape her own work. Later she studied in Paris with the portraitist Jacques-Emile Blanche and the Spaniard Claudio Castelucho. She soon became part of the circle around Gertrude Stein that included Pablo Picasso, Georges Braque, Henri Matisse, and other Fauves and Cubists. A solo exhibiton of Peterson's work in 1908 at the Société des Artistes Français attracted many visitors, including one who arranged a show at the St. Botolph Club in Boston the next year.

In the summer of 1909, the artist began to study with Joaquín Sorolla y Bastida in Madrid, an experience that gave new brilliance and spontaneity to her work. On a trip to Egypt and Algiers that same year, she met Mrs. Theodore Shawe, a wealthy Chicagoan, who persuaded Peterson to return with her to the Midwest. A major show of eighty-seven views of Venice, Spain, Algeria, and Egypt was held at the Art Institute of Chicago in 1910. Sorolla arrived soon after to open his own exhibition at the Institute, and he persuaded Peterson to follow him to New York, where he had been commissioned to do a portrait of Louis Comfort Tiffany. At Tiffany's invitation, Peterson joined the artistic circle at Laurelton, his summer estate in Oyster Bay, Long Island.

The artist's favorite subjects during the months at Laurelton were the lush gardens surrounding the enormous mansion. *Vedder's Fountain, Tiffany's Garden* is one of the works executed at the Tiffany home, a portion of which is visible at the very top of the painting. A high horizon line allows the artist to fill the vertical canvas with the colorful hillside plantings that form the backdrop to the foreground pool. From the near side of the elliptical retaining wall, we view the statuary and cascading stream of the fountain named for the artist Elihu Vedder, who collaborated with Tiffany on many decorative projects, including stained glass and fountain designs.

Peterson's brilliant use of pigment in *Vedder's Fountain*—Impressionistic daubs of green, yellow, and lavender in the foliage contrasted with smooth, velvety strokes in the water—reveals the joy she felt for the garden subject. "The reason I paint flowers," she once wrote, "is because of all things in the world, I think flowers the most beautiful . . . Nature has expended on them a marvelous wealth of color—they scintillate the prismatic hues of the rainbow; they harmonize the pastel shades of the night; they are all that is delicate; all that is lurid, brilliant, bizarre."[1]

Vedder's Fountain is a superb example of Peterson's art, a painting overflowing with the richness and variety of nature's bounty.

Laurene Buckley

1. Jane Peterson quoted in J. Jonathan Joseph, *Jane Peterson: An American Artist* (Boston: J. Jonathan Joseph, 1981), p. 106.

Maurice Prendergast (1861–1924)

19. *Under the Trees*, ca. 1907–1910

Oil on canvas
23 × 28 inches
Signed lower right: *Prendergast*

Provenance:
The artist
to Charles Prendergast, the artist's brother, 1924
to (Kraushaar Galleries, New York), 1932
to (Biltmore, Los Angeles), 1946
Mr. and Mrs. Bruce Kelham
to (Hirschl & Adler Galleries, New York), 1966
to Mr. and Mrs. Ralph Spencer, 1966

Exhibited (partial list):
Art Institute of Chicago, *Special Exhibitions: Paintings by Maurice Prendergast*, 17 March–24 April 1925, no. 7.
Kraushaar Galleries, New York, *Memorial Exhibition of Paintings and Watercolors by Maurice Prendergast*, 16 February–4 March 1925, no. 14.
Cleveland Museum of Art, *Maurice Prendergast Memorial Exhibition*, 15 January–15 February 1926, no. 16.
Albright Art Gallery, Buffalo, *Twenty-sixth Annual Exhibit: American Art*, 17 April–29 May 1932, no. 64.
Whitney Museum of American Art, New York, *Maurice Prendergast Memorial Exhibition*, 21 February–22 March 1934, no. 129.
San Francisco Museum of Modern Art, *Twenty-fifth Anniversary Exhibition: Modern Masters in West Coast Collections*, 18 October–27 November 1960.
Davis & Long Company, New York, *Charles Conder, Robert Henri, James Morrice, Maurice Prendergast: The Formative Years, Paris, 1890's*, 13–31 May 1975, no. 39.

Literature:
Hedley Howell Rhys, "Maurice Prendergast: The Sources and Development of His Style," Ph.D. dissertation, Harvard University, 1952, p. 153.
Carol Clark, Nancy Mowll Mathews, and Gwendolyn Owens, *Maurice Brazil Prendergast, Charles Prendergast: A Catalogue Raisonné* (Munich: Prestel, 1989), no. 234, p. 259 ill.

IN MAY of 1907, Maurice Prendergast left Boston, embarking on what would be his fourth trip abroad. Arriving at the port of Le Havre, France, he went directly to Paris, remaining there for several weeks. With the advent of warmer weather he moved on to the resort town of St. Mâlo, on the coast of Brittany, where he spent his days painting and sketching the lighthouse and crowded beaches. Prendergast returned to Paris in the fall, just as the new art season was getting underway.

This trip marked an important turning point in Prendergast's development, reinforcing his growing tendency to experiment with color and form. Shortly after arriving in Paris, he saw and was deeply influenced by the exhibition of Paul Cézanne's watercolors on view at the Galerie Bernheim-Jeune. He was again exposed to Cézanne's work in October, when he viewed the large retrospective at the Salon d'Automne. On visits to other exhibitions, Prendergast also heightened his familiarity with the whole of the French vanguard, the Fauve painters in particular.

Writing to his Boston patron, Mrs. Oliver Williams, just prior to his return to America in late October, Prendergast acknowledged the impact of his Parisian experience. Referring to the vivid colorism of the Fauves, he declared "I wish we had some of it in Boston or New York."[1] However, his most prophetic remarks, in terms of his own future direction, concerned Cézanne. On the watercolors he had seen in the spring, Prendergast noted that the Frenchman "left everything to the imagination," and that his paintings "were great for their sympathy and suggestive qualities."[2] He went on to declare: "I got what I came over for, a new impulse. I was somewhat bewildered when I first got here, but I think that Cézanne will influence me more than the others."[3] Over the next few years, Prendergast manifested this "new impulse" in a number of important landscapes and still lifes, among them *Under the Trees*, painted between 1907 and 1910.

Indicative of Prendergast's continuing exploration of the theme of outdoor leisure activity, *Under the Trees* depicts an array of figures, most of them female, promenading in a park at the edge of a body of water. Taking his cue from the Cézanne, Prendergast imparts a sense of solidity to his forms with a heavy impasto—dragging, daubing and sometimes scumbling his pigment along the canvas. This approach, quite different from the fluid washes of his earlier watercolors, roots his forms to the ground and gives an overall structural unity to the composition. At the same time, a heightened degree of abstraction is achieved

through the elimination of detail in the faces and costumes of the figures and through the use of dark contour lines, whose broken edges not only add linear definition but also establish a series of surface tensions between figure and ground. The luminous chromaticism, applied in a seemingly arbitrary manner, also enhances the magical "unreality" of the scene.

In *Under the Trees*, we are given a glimpse of contemporary life as perceived by one of the first American artists inspired by early twentieth-century modernism—an aesthetic that stressed, above all else, a subjective interpretation of nature. Thus, informed by the tenets of European Post-Impressionism and guided by his intuition, Prendergast takes us beyond the physical representation of nature, evoking, through the manipulation of line, color, and form, the joyous sensation of a day at a seaside park.[4]

Carol Lowrey

1. Maurice B. Prendergast, Paris, to Mrs. Oliver Williams, Boston, 10 October 1907, Esther Williams Papers, Archives of American Art, Smithsonian Institution, Washington, D.C.
2. Prendergast to Williams.
3. Prendergast to Williams.
4. Inspired by Impressionism and Post-Impressionism, Prendergast began painting views of crowded streets, parks and seaside resorts while in France during the early 1890s. This penchant for festive holiday themes dominated his art throughout his career, given further reinforcement by the example of Edouard Vuillard and Pierre Bonnard of the Nabis, and the Fauvist painters, Raoul Dufy and Albert Marquet. Prendergast derived his imagery from the streets of Boston, Paris, Venice, and Rome as well as from resort towns along the coasts of France and New England.
  Although the site in *Under the Trees* remains unidentified, the work may represent a view of Salem Willows, a seaside locale on the Massachusetts coastline where Prendergast frequently painted. See, for example, Carol Clark's essay on Prendergast's *Landscape with Figures*, ca. 1910–1912, in *Masterworks of American Art from the Munson-Williams-Proctor Institute* (New York: Harry N. Abrams, 1989), p. 110. Prendergast also produced other versions of this scene, including *Under the Trees (Number 2)*, ca. 1914 (Whitney Museum of American Art, New York) and *Under the Trees*, ca. 1913–1915 (Phillips Collection, Washington, D.C.), achieving an even stronger sense of abstraction through the flattening of space and the distortion of form.

Prendergast

William Trost Richards (1833–1905)

20. *Pastoral Landscape*, ca. 1878–1880

Watercolor on paper
8½ × 11½ inches

Provenance:
Estate of the artist
to Thomas Richards, the artist's brother
to C. Nelson Richards, III, the artist's great nephew
to Estate of C. Nelson Richards, III
to (Spanierman Gallery, New York), as of 1966
to Mr. and Mrs. Ralph Spencer, 1966

Exhibited:
Whitney Museum of American Art, New York,
*Eighteenth and Nineteenth Century American Art
from Private Collections*, 27 June–11 September
1972, no. 59.

ON THE BASIS OF stylistic analysis and the English look of the wooded, albeit thoroughly civilized, landscape it portrays, this watercolor may be dated to circa 1878 to 1880, the period of William Trost Richards's first sojourn of length in England. The work may thus be seen in light of the conscious reexamination of the watercolor medium that Richards undertook during those years. This modest but charming painting from the hand of one of America's most renowned watercolorists of the nineteenth century is undocumented. As the absence of signature and date may indicate, it was probably never exhibited, remaining instead among the contents of Richards's studio at the time of his death and later passing into the family of the artist's brother.

The evolution of Richards's watercolor technique is well known.[1] His works from the 1860s demonstrate his affinity for minutely detailed studies and reveal his appreciation for the aesthetic advanced by the famed English critic John Ruskin, whose *The Elements of Drawing* (1857) provided the theoretical impetus for the American Pre-Raphaelite group the Association for the Advancement of Truth in Art, of which Richards was a member. The delicate, stippled brushwork of the 1860s gave way to denser color and facture after 1874, when Richards took to mixing chinese white with his colors to portray his Newport coastal scenes. The result, though less transparent in effect, was a medium more easily handled than pure wash, one that permitted the artist to stretch the limitations of watercolor and to work on a larger scale. By the mid- to late 1870s, Richards's experiments had led to the creation of large gouaches on rough carpet paper— works that compared favorably in size and appearance with oil paintings and challenged their popularity in an active and burgeoning art market.

Among the reasons for Richards's first trip to England were his desire to explore a new market for his work and a wish to expand his visual repertoire. Although he was most often occupied with capturing the spectacular Cornwall seacoast, he was also attracted to the quieter aspects of Britain's topography, which this watercolor appears to portray. Richards studied the work of English watercolorists and expressed his particular admiration for such artists as J. M. W. Turner, Myles Birket Foster, Samuel Prout, and David Cox. It was perhaps because of his diverse tastes that Richards broke away from his almost exclusive use of gouache. This small watercolor testifies to Richards's renewed attention to the more traditional watercolor techniques associated with an earlier generation of artists. While echoes of his initial devotion to Ruskinian detail are present in the carefully delineated, irregular surfaces of the tree trunks and in the lightly stippled foliage of the trees in the middleground, Richards adheres to no single method in this work. This is shown in his use of fine, regular strokes of hatched lines, which moderate the intensity of the blue sky to achieve a greater sense of atmospheric distance beyond the breaking clouds.

In contrast, the treatment of the foreground is uncharacteristically loose in its summarily rendered indications of tufts of grass laid over a simple wash of color. And, with the exception of a few touches of chinese white to highlight the stone wall and the walk leading to it, Richards also relies on transparent washes of the pure medium to convey the subtle changes of light as the eye moves from open to secluded passages of this peaceful acreage. Thus, through the careful orchestration of hatching, stippling, washes, delicate linear detail, and the measured use of chinese white, Richards creates a nostalgic vision through his method and in the prevailing mood of romanticism, that is gently underscored by the vague forms of the trysting couple on the left.

Barbara Dayer Gallati

1. Linda S. Ferber's pioneering and continuing investigation of Richards's art has resulted in several important publications documenting his career, among them: *William Trost Richards: American Landscape and Marine Painter, 1833–1905*, exh. cat. (New York: Brooklyn Museum, 1973); *William Trost Richards (1833–1905): American Landscape and Marine Painter* (New York: Garland Publishing, 1980); *Tokens of Friendship: Miniature Watercolors by William T. Richards*, exh. cat. (New York: Metropolitan Museum of Art, 1982); and Linda S. Ferber [and] William H. Gerdts, *The New Path: Ruskin and the American Pre-Raphaelites*, exh. cat. (New York: Brooklyn Museum, 1985).

Theodore Robinson (1852–1896)

21. *Girl in the Orchard*, ca. 1889

Watercolor on paper
13⅞ × 7¾ inches
Signed lower right: *Th. Robinson*

Provenance:
(Macbeth Gallery, New York)
C. S. McDonough, 1919
to (Frank K. M. Rehn, New York), 1920
to Duncan Phillips, Washington, D.C., 1920
to (Frank K. M. Rehn, New York), 1923
to William H. Bender, Jr., Bronxville, New York, 1962
(Sotheby Parke Bernet, New York, 21 April 1977,
    no. 70)
to Mr. and Mrs. Ralph Spencer, 1977

Exhibited:
Metropolitan Museum of Art, New York, *200 Years of
    Watercolor Painting in America: An Exhibition
    Commemorating the Centennial of the American
    Watercolor Society*, 8 December 1966–29 January
    1967, no. 101 (lent by Mr. and Mrs. William
    H. Bender, Jr.).

Literature:
John I. H. Baur, *Theodore Robinson, 1852–1896*, exh.
    cat. (New York: Brooklyn Museum, 1946), p. 85,
    no. 315 as *Peasant Girl by Tree*; also listed,
    p. 84, no. 299 as *Girl in Orchard*, both listings in
    the checklist of the artist's works, not in the
    exhibition.

This work will be included in the forthcoming
catalogue raisonné of the work of Theodore
Robinson by Ira Spanierman and Sona Johnston.

D URING THE 1870s Theodore Robinson pursued formal instruction at the National Academy of Design and, like many of his compatriots, in the Parisian ateliers of the academic painters Emile-Auguste Carolus-Duran and Jean-Léon Gérôme. His return to New York in 1879 was followed by a period of varied activity that included teaching and employment with John La Farge and Prentice Treadwell, who were providing decorative murals for public and private buildings throughout the city. From 1884 until 1892 Robinson made extended visits to France. Attracted initially to the artists' colonies at Barbizon, he soon became a convert to Impressionism, and at Giverny he developed a close, enduring friendship with Claude Monet. Unlike the French master, whose paintings are often filled with vivid color and radiant light that dissolves outlines in shimmering atmosphere, Robinson recorded nature in more muted tonalities, the forms remaining solid and firmly defined.

Through much of his career, Robinson appears to have been attracted to the French peasant girl as a subject. Whether engaged in one of her numerous daily tasks or pausing to rest and contemplate, she is infused with strength and quiet dignity. The late 1880s, when the artist was evolving his personal style of Impressionism, are especially rich in such images, which were painted in the woods and gardens in and around Giverny.

Girl in the Orchard belongs to this group of pictures. Probably executed about 1889, it depicts a young woman in three-quarter view examining an aspect of the fruit tree nearby. Her brown hair, pinned up, deep pink skirt, and gray bodice suggest that she may be Yvonne, a local woman who is known to have posed for a number of the Giverny paintings. The setting of the work might well be a neighbor's garden in the village, favored by the artist and seen in well-known figural canvases including *Day Dreams*, 1889 (location unknown), *The Layette*, ca. 1891 (Corcoran Gallery of Art, Washington, D.C.), and related pictures, and *In the Garden*, ca. 1889 (The Westmoreland Museum of Art, Greensburg, Pennsylvania).

As the primary vertical element in the composition, the figure, her head in profile against the mottled foliage, is in noticeable contrast to the undulating tree trunk and branches. Although intimate in feeling, the watercolor conveys a certain monumentality, which is evident in other of Robinson's figurative paintings of the period and would appear to relate to the decorative murals on which he worked under La Farge and Treadwell.

Unlike several of the canvases from the late 1880s that explore more subtle chromatic harmonies, this work records with animated brushstrokes a lively juxtaposition of varied colors. While the curve of the tree trunk reflects the warm tones of the skirt, the leaves, shown in veiled washes of clear blues, yellows, and greens, capture the essence of a warm bright summer's day in the French countryside.

During his brief life, Theodore Robinson produced watercolors marked by great delicacy and refinement. Primarily figural, they are accomplished, fully developed paintings that reveal a superb draftsmanship and acute sensibility to color. *Girl in the Orchard*, once owned by Duncan Phillips of Washington, D.C., typifies his best efforts in this small but exquisite body of work.

Sona Johnston

Theodore Robinson

22. *White Bridge on the Canal*, 1893

Oil on canvas
15 × 22 inches

Provenance:
Hamline Robinson, the artist's brother
to Mrs. C. F. Terhune, the artist's niece, Kansas City, Missouri
to Mrs. Gordon Thompson, the artist's grandniece, Evansville, Indiana
(Spanierman Gallery, New York), as of 1966
to Mr. and Mrs. Ralph Spencer, 1966

Exhibited:
Kennedy Galleries, New York, *Theodore Robinson, American Impressionist (1852–1896)*, Winter 1966 (pp. 14, 20 ill.).
Whitney Museum of American Art, New York, *Eighteenth and Nineteenth Century American Art from Private Collections*, 27 June–11 September 1972, no. 62.
National Gallery of Art, Washington, D.C., *American Impressionist Painting*, 1 July–26 August 1973, no. 52 (p. 117 ill.). Circulating exhibition, 1973–1974.
Henry Art Gallery, University of Washington, Seattle, *American Impressionism*, 3 January–2 March 1980, no. 97 (p. 152 ill.). Circulating exhibition, 1980.

Literature:
John I. H. Baur, *Theodore Robinson, 1852–1896*, exh. cat. (New York: Brooklyn Museum, 1946), p. 80, no. 258 in checklist of the artist's works.
William H. Gerdts, *American Impressionism* (New York: Abbeville Press, 1984), pp. 152, 154 col. ill.

This work will be included in the forthcoming catalogue raisonné of the work of Theodore Robinson by Ira Spanierman and Sona Johnston.

WITH HIS RETURN to New York in December 1892, Theodore Robinson ended his French period. During lengthy sojourns at Giverny in the 1880s and early 1890s, he had evolved his own Impressionist style in which he now sought to interpret scenes of his homeland. Particularly successful in this regard are the paintings he executed in the mid-1890s at Napanoch, a small village in New York, on the Connecticut shore, and in his native Vermont.

In July 1893, Robinson was engaged to teach a class at the Brooklyn Art School at Napanoch, a town in the Shawangunk Mountains near the small canal that joined the Delaware and Hudson Rivers.[1] In a series of landscape and genre views painted during the summer months and into the autumn, he recorded life along the waterway. Often, in a manner recalling Claude Monet's series paintings, he would repeat the same view, working at different times of day and under varying weather conditions, noting the subtle changes in color and quality of light.

A structure of particular interest to him was a white bridge that spanned the canal as it made a sweeping curve through the village at the base of a foothill. Extant canvases and notations Robinson made in his diary indicate that he painted the view at least twice.

White Bridge on the Canal, probably executed during September and October of 1893, records the changing season as the foliage turns from the verdant green of summer to rich autumn hues. On the 15th of September 1893, the artist noted in his diary:

> To the white bridge—worked on grey day, but trying to keep my first impression—a very luminous sky and water—difficult as there many kinds of greyness. . . .[2]

Sensitive observations of the nuances of light and reflected color, apparent throughout the canvas, are especially noticeable in the warm, buff-toned foreground, highlighted with touches of peach and lavender, and in the shimmering surface of the water. Passages of brilliant orange at the center, beneath the bridge, and vivid yellow-green along the curved edge of the canal add striking focal points to the painting.

A most impressive aspect of the work is the beautifully constructed composition, in which the various components are reduced to geometric planes and carefully placed to enhance the white bridge at the center of the canvas. That Robinson was especially concerned at this time with refining the unifying elements in his work is evident in a diary notation made earlier in the summer:

> I realize more and more, the importance of the "ensemble," the whole thing going together, thinking quickly, grasping the whole, and working from one part to another, sky to reflection of sky, distance to foreground.[3]

Such self-instructive comments appear frequently in the diaries as the artist labored to adapt his French experience to the landscape of his homeland. Determined to avoid anything artificial or contrived in his art, Robinson rejoiced in the beauty of the ordinary. *White Bridge on the Canal* and the related Napanoch paintings are tranquil glimpses of rural life and testaments to his artistic success during his first summer at home in America.

Sona Johnston

1. Other works painted at Napanoch during the summer and autumn of 1893 include: *Port Ben, Delaware and Hudson Canal* (Pennsylvania Academy of the Fine Arts, Philadelphia), *Evening at the Lock* (private collection, Michigan), and *Port Ben, Delaware and Hudson Canal* (Sheldon Memorial Art Gallery, University of Nebraska, Lincoln).
2. Theodore Robinson Diaries, 15 September 1893, Frick Art Reference Library, New York.
3. Theodore Robinson Diaries, 13 August 1893.

John Singer Sargent (1856–1925)

23. *Spirito Santo, Zattere (Venice, Zattere)*
ca. 1903

Watercolor on paper
10 × 14 inches
Inscribed on verso: *24, Venice, Zattere / J. S. Sargent*

Provenance:
The artist
to William James, Boston
to John James
to (Castano Gallery, Boston), 1961
(Hirschl & Adler Galleries, New York), 1963
to Mr. and Mrs. Ralph Spencer, 1966

Exhibited:
Whitney Museum of American Art, New York,
*Eighteenth and Nineteenth Century American Art
from Private Collections*, 27 June–11 September
1972, no. 59.

This work will be included in the forthcoming
catalogue raisonné of the work of John Singer
Sargent by Richard Ormond and Odile Duff.

JOHN SINGER SARGENT'S lifelong
admiration for Venice began at the age of fourteen,
when he first visited the city with his wealthy
expatriate parents. His earliest mature Venetian works
date from the 1880s and are generally tonal depictions
of dark interiors inhabited by working class figures
who catered to the tourist trade—bead stringers, lace
makers, and glass blowers.

By the turn of the century, Sargent's fame for
portraiture and mural design was at its peak. A
welcome respite from these commissioned projects
came with his annual trips to exotic locales such as the
Middle East, North Africa, and especially Venice,
which he visited nearly every summer between 1902
and 1913. Sargent's favorite sketching medium on these
holidays was watercolor; it offered him easily portable
equipment and the assurance that the work would be
completed in one sitting. In Venice, he would set off in
a gondola each morning from his hotel or, more often,
from the home of his hosts, Mr. and Mrs. Daniel Curtis
of the Palazzo Barbaro, to explore the canals, bridges,
and architecture lining the myriad waterways.

Spirito Santo, Zattere, a painting of the first
decade of the twentieth century, was probably executed
on one of these gondola excursions, since most of
Sargent's loosely handled watercolors were done from a
swaying boat (many even include the prow of the
gondola in the foreground).[1] A carefully selected view
of the lower facade of the Spirito Santo church fills the
visual field. Located at the Fondamenta Zattere along
the busy Giudecca Canal, the site is the starting point
for a festival procession of boats held every July to
commemorate the year of the pestilence. Sargent
captures the Baroque structure from an oblique angle,
pulling the viewer into the scene along its lower pier
and toward the jumble of moored boats beyond.
Nearly obscured by the details of the masts and figures
is the distant campanile of San Marco.[2]

The artist's extraordinary versatility with the
watercolor medium can be clearly seen in *Spirito
Santo, Zattere*. A few sketchy pencil lines were used to
indicate the initial design layout, followed by broad
washes of light blue, green, and beige spread over the
moistened paper. While still wet, the sky was streaked
with touches of slightly richer blue and pink to
represent billowing cumulus clouds that hover over the
scene. After allowing the paper to dry, Sargent then
applied a second wash of his favorite sienna brown and
ultramarine blue for the shaded areas of the church
facade and the darkened shadows at the water's edge.
A deeper brown provided the final touches of rippling

waves, the maze of dancing masts, and the details of
windows and pediments. Drybrush was added in
strategic places to replicate the stuccoed surfaces and a
last wash of brilliant turquoise fills the opening of the
doorway. The total effect is one of spontaneity—a
scene glimpsed and committed to paper with a
freshness that remains to the present day.

Unlike the panoramic views of the Venetian
cityscape executed by Antonio Canaletto, J. M. W.
Turner, and the American Thomas Moran, Sargent's
architectural views have more in common with James
McNeill Whistler's earlier vignettes of the city—
abbreviated glimpses of doorways and facades that
often include local inhabitants. Sargent's fragmented
architectural views, however, usually eschew the figure
and are even more focused in their close-up, de-
historicizing renderings. The palette, as in *Spirito
Santo, Zattere*, represents Sargent at his most vivid,
showing the lasting influence of his earlier exposure to
French Impressionism. Out of an intimate knowledge
of the ageless city of Venice, Sargent created a new,
dazzling vocabulary of midday splendor. As T. Martin
Wood said of the artist in 1946:

> He is one of the few painters who [has]
> faced the noon . . . His brush has given it in
> water-colours the finest interpretation it has
> yet received.[3]

Laurene Buckley

1. The disparity in Sargent's watercolors between those produced on
solid ground versus the works executed from a boat is discussed by a
number of scholars. See, for example, Annette Blaugrund, "'Sunshine
Captured': The Development and Dispersement of Sargent's
Watercolors," in Patricia Hills et al, *John Singer Sargent*, exh. cat. (New
York: Whitney Museum of American Art in association with Harry
N. Abrams, 1986), pp. 228–229. For further information on Sargent in
Venice, see Linda Ayres, "Sargent in Venice," in Hills et al, *John Singer
Sargent*, pp. 49–73. Also useful are the two studies by Margaretta
M. Lovell: *Venice: The American View, 1860–1920*, exh. cat. (San
Francisco: Fine Arts Museums of San Francisco, 1984); and *A
Visitable Past: Views of Venice by American Artists, 1860–1915*
(Chicago: University of Chicago Press, 1989).
2. Another view of the exact scene, in blue tones, is *All' Ave Maria*,
ca. 1907 (The Brooklyn Museum). See Donelson F. Hoopes, *Sargent
Watercolors* (New York: Watson-Guptill, 1970), p. 18. Hoopes
misidentifies the campanile as that of San Giorgio Maggiore; see p. 56.
3. T. Martin Wood, *John Singer Sargent* (New York: Frederick
A. Stokes, 1946), p. 64.

John Henry Twachtman (1853–1902)

24. *Moonlight, Flanders*, ca. 1885

Pastel on paper
7½ × 14½ inches
Signed lower right: *J. H. Twachtman*

Provenance:
Godfrey Twachtman, the artist's son, Independence,
   Missouri
to (Spanierman Gallery, New York), as of 1968
to Mr. and Mrs. Ralph Spencer, 1968

Exhibited:
Cincinnati Art Museum, *John Henry Twachtman:
A Retrospective Exhibition*, 7 October–20
November 1966, no. 93, (p. 30 ill.).
Ira Spanierman Gallery, New York, *John Henry
Twachtman, 1853–1902: An Exhibition of
Paintings and Pastels*, 3–24 February 1968, no. 25.

Literature:
John Douglass Hale, *The Life and Creative
Development of John H. Twachtman*, 2 vols., Ph.D.
dissertation, Ohio State University, Columbus,
1957, (Ann Arbor, Mich.: University Microfilms
International, 1958), no. 997, p. 591 (as *Moonlight
on the Water*).

This work will be included in the forthcoming
catalogue raisonné of the work of John Henry
Twachtman by Ira Spanierman and Lisa
N. Peters.

JOHN HENRY TWACHTMAN displayed pastels for the first time publicly in January 1886, in a solo exhibition held at J. Eastman Chase's Gallery in Boston. It seems likely that he had begun to explore the medium during the previous summer, most of which was spent in Holland. The majority of the oil paintings shown at Chase's presented Dutch subjects, and although only one of the eight pastels *Mills at Dordrecht*, is identified with a specific locale, the others probably also depicted Dutch scenes. Among the pastels were three nocturnal pictures, works in a genre Twachtman had not previously explored and never would again. These were *Late Twilight, Sunset,* and *Moonlight*. The last is undoubtedly the work now known as *Moonlight, Flanders*.

Although the site depicted in *Moonlight, Flanders* is not immediately recognizable as Holland—there are no windmills or other characteristic landmarks—a number of Twachtman's Dutch oils, watercolors, and etchings feature similar views across watery chasms broken only by thin strips of land. It is probable that this work shows a view from Dordrecht, looking across the river Maas towards the towns of Ablassadam and Pappendrecht.

Moonlight, Flanders is one of Twachtman's most spiritualized depictions, conveying the solace of nature and inducing the viewer to enter a transient realm between day and night. The very minimal treatment elicits a mood of quiet meditation. The surface of the paper is covered with a layer of lavender chalk, evoking the low light and hazy atmosphere of dusk. The moon subtly emerges from the mist, emitting a faint yellow glow and casting a gentle reflection on the water. The scene is given definition by the shadowy land masses that mark the horizon line.

Twachtman adds to the work's tranquil harmony by accentuating its pictorial coordinates and thereby creating an abstract design. The strips of land repeat the horizontal format of the work and seem to lay flat against its surface. These are delicately balanced by the upright pilings, which establish the picture's vertical axis and lead into space. Many of the elements of *Moonlight, Flanders* suggest that Twachtman had been influenced by the Venetian pastels of James McNeill Whistler. Although Twachtman was probably not in Venice during Whistler's famous eleven-month trip to the city during 1879–1880, he would have become familiar with Whistler's approach through mutual friends, such as Robert Blum and Otto Bacher, who had met the older artist and adopted his style. However, there is also evidence to suggest that

Twachtman had not yet studied Whistler's drawings firsthand; his application of pastel in *Moonlight, Flanders* is heavier than in Whistler's Venetian works. Twachtman appears to have transferred to pastel the method he was using at the time for his oils, as in the well-known *Arques-la-Bataille*, 1885 (Metropolitan Museum of Art, New York), in which a thin liquid wash of pigment creates a soft and smooth surface.

There may have been other immediate sources for this work. Views of broad rivers intercepted by land masses treated as linear bands were painted by seventeenth-century Dutch artists such as Salomon van Ruysdael and Jan van Goyen, whose works Twachtman would have seen on visits to the Frans Hals Museum in Haarlem and other public collections.[1] He may have also have been inspired by the moonlit landscapes of Aert van der Neer and others. In addition, Twachtman had met the artist Anton Mauve in 1881 and probably visited with him again in 1885. He would therefore have been familiar with the work of the contemporary Dutch painters associated with the Hague School. Working out of doors, artists such as Mauve, Jan Hendrik Weissenbruch, and Jacob Maris rendered casual rural landscapes, conveying their immediate responses to nature while seeking to capture its inherent order. Twachtman's French period paintings, which date from 1883 to 1885, share many similarities with the silvery toned depictions of hazy, damp days created by Hague School artists.

Twachtman's synthesized a number of artistic modes in *Moonlight, Flanders*. However, the work also reflects the artist's own evolving stylistic concerns—his development of a plein-air approach to the landscape and his emerging interest in capturing evanescent and delicate qualities in nature.

Lisa N. Peters

1. Twachtman signed the visitor's book at the Frans Hals Museum in Haarlem on 11 June 1885 and again on 5 September 1885. See Petra ten-Doesschate Chu, "Nineteenth-Century Visitors to the Frans Hals Museum," in *The Documented Image: Visions in Art History*, ed. Gabriel P. Weisberg and Laurinda S. Dixon (Syracuse, N. Y.: Syracuse University Press, 1987), pp. 111-144.

John Henry Twachtman

25. *Newport Harbor*, ca. 1889

Pastel on paper
12 × 9½ inches
Signed lower right: *J. H. Twachtman*

Provenance:
(Maynard Walker Galleries, New York), as of 1966
to Mr. and Mrs. Ralph Spencer, 1967

Exhibited:
Cincinnati Art Museum, *John Henry Twachtman: A Retrospective Exhibition*, 7 October–20 November 1966, no. 110 (p. 31 ill.).
Ira Spanierman Gallery, New York, *John Henry Twachtman, 1853–1902: An Exhibition of Paintings and Pastels*, 3–24 February 1968, no. 34 [p. 19, ill.].

This work will be included in the forthcoming catalogue raisonné of the work of John Henry Twachtman by Ira Spanierman and Lisa N. Peters.

BETWEEN HIS return from Europe in late 1885 and his move to Greenwich, Connecticut, in approximately the fall of 1889, John Henry Twachtman appears to have led a nomadic existence and produced little art. The exception was his visit to Newport, Rhode Island, in the summer of 1889, when he created an important group of works.

Twachtman may have been attracted to Newport because of its long history as an artists' colony—John La Farge, who arrived in Newport in 1859 drew many artists to the charming coastal town. Twachtman's visit could also have been prompted by an invitation to teach. As indicated in the diary of Anna Hunter, an artist who ran a school in Newport, Twachtman taught Hunter and a number of other students during his stay.[1] A significant development appears to have occurred both in Twachtman's methods of instruction and in his art while in Newport. Hunter records that Twachtman was giving lessons in her studio in early June. By the twenty-first of the month, however, the artist was taking his students outside: "Studio in morning. Mr. Twachtman wishes us to begin big canvas out of doors," wrote Hunter.[2] Twachtman's class was perhaps the first in plein-air painting in America, preceding even that of William Merritt Chase in Shinnecock, Long Island.

Twachtman's own art also benefited from working in the open air. Although Hunter mentions Twachtman executing canvases, most of the Newport works known today are watercolors and pastels. His explorations of both media, which are especially amenable to a spontaneous, direct approach, led to the creation of a group of sparkling and original pictures. *Waterside Scene* (Mead Art Museum, Amherst, Massachusetts), which features a Newport pier, is perhaps Twachtman's crispest and freshest watercolor, and *Newport Harbor* is among his most refined and delightful pastels.

Newport Harbor depicts a sailboat anchored alongside a shore lined with warehouses. Rather than focusing on picturesque aspects of the subject, Twachtman concentrates on the abstract properties of his scene. Using delicate and varied strokes, he captures the interplay of line and shape and shifting qualities of light and air. The boat, viewed from an oblique angle, curves boldly and graciously into the space. Its plunging diagonal is restrained, however, by the gently outlined and shaded buildings on the shore, which reinforce the work's angular contours and flat surface. Twachtman expresses the sinuous beauty of the boat's shape with a sustained streak of white chalk. The flickering reflections and shadows on the water are

rendered with staccato dashes of color. The brown of the paper is brought into the design, with light tones blended gently into the background to convey atmospheric and luminous properties.

Newport Harbor demonstrates a progression in Twachtman's pastel aesthetic. In European works from the mid-1880s, such as as *Moonlight, Flanders* (pl. 24), he covered his surfaces with a smooth layer of chalk. Here he takes more advantage of the medium's suitability to sketching. This stylistic shift reveals Twachtman's familiarity with James McNeill Whistler's pastels, which had been featured in a large show at Wunderlich Gallery in New York in March 1889. Indeed, when Twachtman's Newport pastels were shown at the same venue in May 1890, at the fourth exhibition of the Society of American Painters in Pastel, the press pointed out relationships between the two artists. One critic went so far as to note of Twachtman's pastels: "All it need hardly be said, were clever, and had they been signed with the Whistlerian 'butterfly,' it would have seemed all right."[3]

Yet Twachtman's pastels were perhaps not as "clever" as those of the well-known American expatriate. Works such as *Newport Harbor* are neither as broadly treated as Whistler's panoramic views of Venetian waterways nor as detailed, highly patterned, or consciously artistic as his depictions of the streets of Venice and London. Twachtman used pastel primarily as a means of expressing plein-air experience. The directness of the medium suited his desire to convey transitive and fleeting qualities in nature. Reviewing the 1890 pastel exhibition, one critic perceptively stated. "Among the twenty-nine contributors of the eighty-nine drawings, not one appears to have hit the right method of using pastels better than Mr. J. H. Twachtman. He uses paper of different shades—brownish, greenish, grayish, or pale straw, and does not elaborate and insist too much on his picture. [His] delightful marines are touched in with spirit. . . ."[4]

Lisa N. Peters

1. See Hunter Family Diaries, box 98, vault A, Archives, Newport Historical Society, Newport, R.I.
2. Hunter Family Diaries, 21 June 1889.
3. "The Pastel Exhibition," *Art Amateur* 23 (June 1890): 4.
4. "Painters in Pastel," *New York Times*, 5 May 1890, p. 4.

John Henry Twachtman

26. *Frozen Brook*, ca. 1893

Oil on canvas
30 × 22 inches
Signed lower left: *J. H. Twachtman*

Provenance:
(American Art Galleries, New York, *Sale of the Work of
the Late John H. Twachtman*, 19 March 1903, no. 41)
to Dr. Alexander C. Humphreys
to (American Art Association, New York, 14–15
February 1917)
to (Macbeth Gallery, New York)
to Ruth and Albert E. McVitty, 1918
to Estate of Ruth McVitty, Princeton, New Jersey
to (Spanierman Gallery, New York), 1969
to Mr. and Mrs. Ralph Spencer, 1969

Exhibited (partial list):
Buffalo Fine Arts Academy, Albright Art Gallery, New
York, *Inaugural Loan Collection of Paintings*,
31 May–1 July 1905, no. 223.
Lotos Club, New York, *Paintings from the Collection of
Alexander Humphries*, 30 March-early April 1907,
no. 72.
New York School of Applied Design for Women,
Fifty Paintings by the Late John H. Twachtman,
15 January–15 February 1913, no. 33.
Munson-Williams-Proctor Institute, Utica, New York,
*Presenting the Work of John H. Twachtman,
American Painter*, 5–28 November 1939, no. 7.
Whitney Museum of American Art, New York,
*Eighteenth and Nineteenth Century American Art
from Private Collections*, 27 June–11 September
1972, no. 69.
National Gallery of Art, Washington, D. C., *John
Twachtman: Connecticut Landscapes*, 15 October
1989–28 January 1990, no. 7.

Literature:
Charles de Kay, "John H. Twachtman," *Art World and
Arts and Decoration* 9 (June 1918): 73, 75 ill.
Allen Tucker, *John H. Twachtman* (New York: Whitney
Museum of American Art, 1931), p. 23 ill.
Deborah Chotner, Lisa N. Peters, and Kathleen A.
Pyne, *John Twachtman: Connecticut Landscapes*,
exh. cat. (Washington, D.C.: National Gallery of
Art, 1989), pp. 30, 55, 77 ill., 95 col. ill.

This work will be included in the forthcoming
catalogue raisonné of the work of John Henry
Twachtman by Ira Spanierman and Lisa N. Peters.

ALTHOUGH WINTER scenes were rarely
depicted by the painters of the Hudson River
School, toward the end of the nineteenth
century, as artists sought to express intimate and
spiritual qualities in nature, the subject achieved a new
vogue. The Tonalists were especially fond of rendering
snow-covered rural sites, often at twilight or dawn,
finding in them a means of conveying introspective,
pensive moods. Birge Harrison, for example, wrote
that "considered in terms of color and decorative line,
winter is far more beautiful than summer . . . after all
it is the snow which gives our winter landscape its
greatest beauty."[1] Throughout his career, John Henry
Twachtman essayed the subject of winter—he first
exhibited a depiction of it in 1879.[2] However, it is for
the snow scenes he executed during the 1890s at his
home in Greenwich, Connecticut, that he became
renowned as a consummate interpreter of the season.

In *Frozen Brook*, Twachtman captures suggestive
qualities of the landscape. The thick, hazy atmosphere
envelops the scene, creating a stillness broken only by
the sinuous curve of the brook that leads slowly into
the distance. In the desire to express the poetry of
winter Twachtman shared the concerns of the
Tonalists. However, while the Tonalists rendered
images from memory, creating romanticized visions of
nature, Twachtman worked directly from his sites,
executing powerful and tactile depictions that capture
the look and feel of the outdoors environment, its
subtle nuances as well as its imperfections. As a writer
for the *Art Amateur* noted in 1901:

> Twachtman . . . almost invariably selects
> broken ground and cloudy weather. . . He
> seldom attempts to render the delicacy of a
> fresh fall of snow, preferring as a rule, to
> wait a day or two until the snow has begun
> to sink down between the rocks and to
> melt from the higher points.[3]

During his years in Greenwich, Twachtman
developed a versatile and expressive Impressionist
technique that allowed him to convey the particular
qualities of his sites in different weather conditions.
In *Winter Harmony* (National Gallery of Art,
Washington, D.C.), he depicts the icy stillness of mid-
winter; snowdrifts are covered with a slick frozen
surface and the pool at the center of the composition is
glazed over. In *Frozen Brook*, he represents a landscape
in early or late winter. The snow cover is damp and
heavy, barely covering the ground and beginning to
melt along the stream bed. Covering his canvas with

thick white impasto brushed vigorously over layers of
lavender and sea green, Twachtman conveys the
texture of the snow and effects of light and atmosphere
on its surface. The changing rhythm of his brush and
subtle shifts of tone give the work a sensuality not
found in the winter views of other artists of the time.

Twachtman's vantage point also distinguishes his
rendering. In *Frozen Brook* he avoids traditional
perspective ordering. Mauve-tinged snow and heavy
blue-gray clouds blend together, almost entirely
obscuring the border between land and sky. The high
horizon line also forces the image to be read abstractly.
Twachtman further denies a progression into space by
dividing the composition diagonally, with a broad and
flat hillside sweeping upward from left to right,
focusing the viewer's attention on the surface of the
canvas. *Frozen Brook* conjures the chill and frost of
winter, drawing the viewer into the meditative,
quiescent environment; at the same time, the work is
strikingly modern, its boldly patterned design
anticipating twentieth-century modern art.

Frozen Brook may be the same work of this title
included in Twachtman's 1893 exhibition at the
American Art Galleries in New York.[4] As a reviewer
commented on the artist's snow scenes on view: "They
are beautiful pieces of light, air and color—especially
refined color."[5] *Frozen Brook* exemplifies the subtle
majesty of Twachtman's art.

Lisa N. Peters

1. Birge Harrison, "The Appeal of the Winter Landscape," *Fine Art
Journal* 30 (March 1914): 194, 196.
2. Twachtman showed a painting titled *Winter Landscape* at the 54th
annual exhibition of the National Academy of Design, held 31 April–
31 May 1879.
3. "Snow Scenes in Oil Painting," *Art Amateur* 44 (March 1901):
99–100.
4. The show, held in May 1893, included works by Twachtman and
J. Alden Weir. An exhibition of paintings by Claude Monet and Paul
Albert Besnard was simultaneously on view, also at the American Art
Galleries, New York.
5. "Some French and American Pictures," *New York Evening Post*,
8 May 1893, p. 7.

John Henry Twachtman

27. *Boat Landing*, ca. 1900–1902

Oil on panel
13½ × 9½ inches
Stamped lower left in red: *Twachtman Sale*[1]

Provenance:
(American Art Galleries, New York, *Sale of the Work of
the Late John H. Twachtman*, 24 March 1903, no. 3)
to Charles M. Kelly
Private Collection, as of 1959
(Hirschl & Adler Galleries, New York), as of 1968
(Sloan & Roman, New York), as of 1968
to Mr. and Mrs. Ralph Spencer, 1968

Exhibited:
Ira Spanierman Gallery, New York, *Twachtman
in Gloucester: His Last Years, 1900–1902*,
12 May–13 June 1987, no. 15 (p. 79 col. ill.).

Literature:
John Douglass Hale, *The Life and Creative
Development of John H. Twachtman*, 2 vols., Ph.D.
dissertation, Ohio State University, Columbus,
1957 (Ann Arbor, Mich.: University Microfilms
International, 1958), no. 54a, p. 431.

This work will be included in the forthcoming
catalogue raisonné of the work of John Henry
Twachtman by Ira Spanierman and Lisa N.
Peters.

DURING THE LAST three summers of John Henry Twachtman's life, spent in Gloucester, Massachusetts, the artist created some of his most advanced, innovative, and vibrant works.[2] Although he was undoubtedly drawn to Gloucester because of its beauty—its picturesque harbors and craggy shoreline had been painted by countless artists, beginning with Fitz Hugh Lane in the 1840s—the town also offered him another attraction. It provided him with the chance to be reunited with his old friend Frank Duveneck and with other colleagues from earlier in his career.

Among those in Gloucester during the summers of 1900 to 1902 were many who, like Twachtman, had studied in Munich in the 1870s, including Duveneck, Joseph DeCamp, Theodore Wendel, and Charles Corwin. This gathering surely inspired Twachtman's return to the direct and spontaneous approach that had characterized his Munich style. In Gloucester, Twachtman abandoned the layered effects evident in his Greenwich landscapes, instead rendering subjects *alla prima* (all at once), with little retouching.

This method is especially apparent in *Boat Landing*. Twachtman created this work directly on a thin red panel (probably from one of the cigar-box tops he often used as supports while in Gloucester), determining his design as he painted, in the process giving life and energy to the depiction. His brushwork expresses his vision of the scene: the foreground pier on which he stood is radically foreshortened, seeming to swing upward with the motion of his forceful strokes. Paint applied in rhythmic and staccato daubs over the red ground conveys vivid colors and effects of light on the water. The middleground pier and warehouses on the opposite shore are treated abstractly, with broad dashes of color left thickly on the surface.

Despite Twachtman's return to the freedom of his Munich manner, the Gloucester works are vastly different from the dark harbor scenes he rendered in the 1870s. He avoids the heavy, dramatic style of Munich, which he had come to consider artificial, instead using bright colors expressive of his direct experience of nature and sunlight.[3]

Further, a significant development in Twachtman's work is exemplified by *Boat Landing*. Whereas his Munich images often appear arbitrarily arranged, the Gloucester works demonstrate the artist's control over his compositional means, his sensitivity to design and his ability to suggest relationships within a landscape that a casual viewer would tend to overlook. The painting is enlivened by a series of triangles that echo throughout the composition. A repetition of orange and peach tones brings together the foreground and background. The boat's irregular shape is answered by the rising corner of the pier at the right. Vertical elements are crossed by horizontals, serving here not to create harmony, but to add to a lively interplay of elements.

In *Boat Landing*, Twachtman avoids the conventions of the traditional marine view, creating an extremely dynamic abstract composition that indicates the direction his art might have taken had he lived longer. The work is one of the artist's most vivid evocations of Gloucester's brilliant light, fresh air, and sparkling color contrasts.

Lisa N. Peters

1. Indicates that the painting was in the sale of Twachtman's estate, held in 1903 at the American Art Galleries, New York.
2. For information on Twachtman's Gloucester period, see John Douglass Hale, Richard J. Boyle, and William H. Gerdts, *Twachtman in Gloucester: His Last Years, 1900–1902*, exh. cat. (New York: Ira Spanierman Gallery, 1987).
3. See Carolyn C. Mase, "John H. Twachtman," *International Studio* 72 (January 1921): lxxiii. Mase wrote of Twachtman: "Once I recollect his showing me a brownish-black water colour, reeking with all the colours that Nature does not show. 'That,' he said with a chuckle, 'is sunny Venice, done under the influence of the Munich School.'"

Julian Alden Weir (1852–1919)

28. *Vase of Flowers*, late 1880s

Oil on canvas
13½ × 15 inches
Signed lower left: *J. Alden Weir*

Provenance:
(Spanierman Gallery, New York), ca. 1966
to Mr. and Mrs. Ralph Spencer, New York, ca. 1966

J. ALDEN WEIR is best known for the Impressionist landscapes and the decorative figural works he rendered from the 1890s through the early twentieth century. From the late 1870s through the end of the next decade, however, Weir focused on still life and established a reputation as an innovator in the genre.[1] The still lifes, especially his depictions of flowers, number among his most delightful and sensual works. They also reflect the many developments in his art during an experimental and pivotal phase of his career.

Vase of Flowers shows a group of freshly picked blossoms, casually arranged in a round earthenware vase. Whereas in many of Weir's floral still lifes he combines elegant containers of china or silver with cultivated blooms (the rose seems to have been his favorite), in this painting, he sets humble field flowers—Queen Anne's lace, thistles, and goldenrod—in a simple vessel. The modest subject as well as the intimate composition suggest the influence of still lifes of the French eighteenth-century master Jean-Baptiste-Siméon Chardin, whose works had been an inspiration to Weir since the mid-1880s. The influence of the work of Henri Fantin-Latour and Edouard Manet, who had initiated the Chardin revival in Europe in the late 1860s, may also be seen in Weir's rendering, in the straightforward arrangement, the neutral background, and the sketchy and suggestive brushwork.

Vase of Flowers demonstrates also the emergence of a more consequential development in Weir's aesthetic. By the late 1880s, Weir had begun to adopt aspects of an Impressionist style. In *Vase of Flowers*, he appears to have mixed paint directly on canvas to depict the background, using his brush vigorously to reveal qualities of light and atmosphere. Varying the thickness of his pigment and the rhythm of his strokes, he conveys the different characteristics of the flowers, delineating the mossy, irregular surface of Queen Anne's lace, the sprightly softness of thistle, and the delicacy of goldenrod.

The legacy of the romantic still lifes of John La Farge is another influence discernable in *Vase of Flowers*. Weir chooses to express suggestive and poetic qualities rather than to represent his subject with the detail and precision seen in the works of the American Pre-Raphaelites. Yet Weir's love for the specific floral types he depicts is apparent. Weir shared his delight in wildflowers with his close friend John Henry Twachtman, who also painted them during the late 1880s and the 1890s.[2]

Vase of Flowers is one of Weir's most sensitive renderings of the floral motif. The artist's informal arrangement and lively brush handling express the feeling of freedom and pleasure that he experienced in seeing this out-of-doors subject brought inside.

Lisa N. Peters

1. Weir's still lifes are discussed in Doreen Bolger Burke, *J. Alden Weir: An American Impressionist*, exh. cat. (Newark, Del.: University of Delaware Press, 1983), pp. 126–142. Burke's book is the standard monograph on Weir.
2. See Lisa N. Peters, et. al., *In the Sunlight: The Floral and Figurative Art of J. H. Twachtman*, exh. cat. (New York: Spanierman Gallery, 1989). Twachtman's *Flowers*, ca. early 1890s (Pennsylvania Academy of the Fine Arts, Philadelphia), illustrated on page 71, resembles Weir's *Vase of Flowers*.

Julian Alden Weir

29. *Vase of Roses*, late 1880s

Pastel on paper
16 × 14 inches
Signed lower right: *J. Alden Weir*

Provenance:
(Milch Galleries, New York)
Mrs. Bernard Spector
(Spanierman Gallery, New York) as of 1968
to Mr. and Mrs. Ralph Spencer, New York, 1968

Exhibited:
Metropolitan Museum of Art, New York, *J. Alden Weir: An American Impressionist*, 14 October 1983–8 January 1984. Circulating exhibition, 1983–1984.

Literature:
Doreen Bolger Burke, *J. Alden Weir: An American Impressionist*, exh. cat. (Newark, Del.: University of Delaware Press, 1983), pp. 173, 174 ill.

VASE OF ROSES was probably rendered in the late 1880s, when J. Alden Weir was concentrating on floral subjects and exploring the medium of pastel. Executed in a grander scale than any of his other pastels *Vase of Roses* is the only known work in which these important interests coalesced.[1]

Weir included roses in some of his finest oils of the 1880s. Many of these were large canvases intended for ornately decorated settings, and thus flowers were often set amidst collections of refined objects, such as silver bowls and German faience jars.[2] In his oils, Weir accentuated the elegance and poetic beauty of the rose, often "enwrapping his flowers in a mist," as the writer Mariana van Rensselaer noted in 1888.[3] In *Vase of Flowers*, Weir presents a straightforward and unglamorized view of the subject, expressing an appreciation for the flower in all its phases. On the left are full and ripe pink blossoms, below which a swollen yellow rose begins to droop. On the right, one bud has shrivelled, while another full flower is partially wilted. The decorative and casual arrangement is enlivened by fresh leafy vines interwoven with the flowers.

The American pastel revival was fully underway by the time Weir began to employ the medium.[4] Although he was a founding member of the Society of Painters in Pastel, he did not participate in the organization's first exhibition in 1885, and it is possible that his initial investigation of pastel took place during the summers of 1887 and 1888, when he spent time with his close friend John Henry Twachtman in Branchville, Connecticut, where Weir's home was located.[5] In depicting scenes of the countryside, both artists used pastel to draw lightly and sparingly on toned papers, creating subtle distinctions between forms and conveying suggestive, atmospheric qualities.

In *Vase of Roses* Weir employs a different approach to pastel. Eschewing the minimal, sketchy mode used for the landscapes, he covers the surface of his paper with chalk and renders forms in a taut, precise manner reminiscent of his oil technique. Weir's training under the French academic painter Jean-Léon Gérôme is evident in the able delineation of space, balanced composition, and adeptly modeled forms. Weir clearly distinguishes textures, contrasting the soft delicacy of the flowers with the sparkling glass surface of the vase. Instead of working quickly, Weir appears to have applied pastel slowly and carefully in *Vase of Roses*, again, approximating his methodical and controlled oil painting approach. The work appears complete and finished, in contrast to Weir's pastel landscapes, in which he often covered surfaces unevenly, allowing the paper's texture to contribute to his schemes. Indeed *Vase of Roses'* unique treatment and bold size suggest that Weir may have intended to display it in an important exhibition.

Weir possibly also chose to modify his pastel technique for a rendering of an indoor motif. (Twachtman's floral pastels depict only outdoor subjects.[6]) But his application of chalk in *Vase of Roses* is neither heavy nor forced. He conveys light reflecting on a background wall by a layering of softly luminescent tones applied with rhythmic downward strokes. The room's atmosphere is evident in his treatment of flowers; their edges seem to blur in the softly lit space. The smooth dark surface of the table is also subtly rendered, with a layering of tones expressing light and shadow.

In *Vase of Roses* Weir combines precise and realistic drawing with a tender and sensitive interpretation. The fresh color of pastel is perfectly suited to the delicate beauty of the subject. *Vase of Roses* is among Weir's best pastels; one wishes there were more known examples of his investigation of the floral subject in the medium.

Lisa N. Peters

1. In her monograph, Doreen Bolger Burke states that *Vase of Roses* is Weir's only known still life executed in pastel. See Burke, *J. Alden Weir: An American Impressionist*, exh. cat. (Newark, Del.: University of Delaware Press, 1983). p. 173.
2. Burke notes that many of Weir's still lifes were commissioned by the decorating firm of Cottier and Co. See Burke, *J. Alden Weir*, pp. 126–142.
3. Mariana van Rensselaer, "Flower and Fruit Pictures at the Academy of Design," *Garden and Forest* 1 (25 April 1888): 107.
4. An in-depth discussion of Weir's pastels is found in Burke, *J. Alden Weir*, pp. 168–175. See also Dianne H. Pilgrim, "The Revival of Pastels in Nineteenth Century America: The Society of Painters in Pastel," *American Art Journal* 10 (November 1978): 43–62; Doreen Bolger et. al., *American Pastels in the Metropolitan Museum of Art*, exh. cat. (New York: Metropolitan Museum of Art, 1989).
5. Weir contributed works to the other three Society of Painters in Pastel exhibitions, in 1888, 1889, and 1890.
6. Information on Twachtman's pastels of flowers may be found in Lisa N. Peters, et. al. *In the Sunlight: The Floral and Figurative Art of J. H. Twachtman*, exh. cat. (New York: Spanierman Gallery, 1989).

Contributors

Richard J. Boyle, art historian and former director, Pennsylvania Academy of the Fine Arts, Philadelphia

Laurene Buckley, Spanierman Gallery research associate and Ph.D. student in art history, Graduate School of the City University of New York

David Park Curry, Ph.D., chief curator and deputy director, Virginia Museum of Fine Arts, Richmond

Charles B. Ferguson, director emeritus, New Britain Museum of American Art, New Britain, Connecticut

Barbara Dayer Gallati, associate curator, American Painting and Sculpture, The Brooklyn Museum, New York

Gregory Gilbert, assistant to the curator of prints and drawings, Jane Voorhies Zimmerli Art Museum, New Brunswick, New Jersey and Ph.D. student in art history, Rutgers University, New Brunswick, New Jersey

Susan Hobbs, Ph.D., Smithsonian research associate and former curator, Freer Gallery of Art, Smithsonian Institution, Washington, D.C. and the National Museum of American Art, Smithsonian Institution, Washington, D.C. and author of the forthcoming catalogue raisonné of the work of Thomas Dewing

William Innes Homer, Ph.D., professor and chairman, Department of Art History, University of Delaware, Wilmington

Sona Johnston, coauthor of the forthcoming catalogue raisonné of the work of Theodore Robinson (with Ira Spanierman)

Carol Lowrey, Spanierman Gallery research associate and Ph.D. student in art history, Graduate School of the City University of New York

Nic Madormo, adjunct professor, Brooklyn College, New York, adjunct professor, Fashion Institute of Technology, New York and Ph.D. student in art history, Graduate School of the City University of New York

Bennard B. Perlman, art critic, *Daily Record*, Baltimore; and professor emeritus and former chairman, Department of Fine and Applied Arts, Community College of Baltimore

Lisa N. Peters, Spanierman Gallery director of research, coauthor of the forthcoming catalogue raisonné of the work of John Henry Twachtman (with Ira Spanierman) and Ph.D. student in art history, Graduate School of the City University of New York

Ronald G. Pisano, art historian and author of the forthcoming catalogue raisonné of the work of William Merritt Chase

James Yarnall, Richard J. Schwartz research associate, Department of American Decorative Arts, The Metropolitan Museum of Art, New York and director of the catalogue raisonné of the work of John La Farge

Index

Published in the United States of America
in 1990 by Spanierman Gallery,
50 East 78th Street, New York, N.Y. 10021

Design: Marcus Ratliff Inc.
Composition: Trufont Typographers, Inc.
Lithography: Thorner-Sidney Press
ISBN: 0-945936-7